The Big 11+

Maths

Play Book

Pathway to Success

The Armadillo's Pillow Ltd

ISBN 978-1-912936-07-6

71-75 Shelton Street
Covent Garden
London, England, WC2H 9JQ
United Kingdom

The Big 11+ Maths Play Book

Contents

The Big 11+ Maths Play Book

Contents

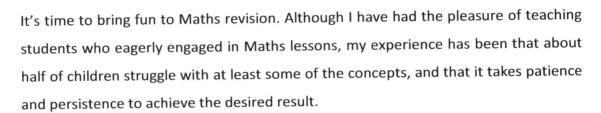

PATHWAY TO SUCCESS
11+ Maths Proficiency

It's time to bring fun to Maths revision. Although I have had the pleasure of teaching students who eagerly engaged in Maths lessons, my experience has been that about half of children struggle with at least some of the concepts, and that it takes patience and persistence to achieve the desired result.

The Big 11+ Maths Play Book has been designed to help make the learning more enjoyable. The sections have been arranged to supplement study, and in many cases, provide some type of game to add a bit of fun to the work.

The best way to increase proficiency in Maths is to practise with a caring yet focused approach. To assist in these goals, this book offers a diverse selection of Maths challenges tailored to expand mathematical skills and improve performance in the Eleven Plus. Note that games and puzzles have also been added, such as Sudoku, that are not part of KS2 or the exam. However, these can improve logical thinking skills that will be very helpful not only for the test, but for further study and success.

The goal of these photocopiable materials is to give your child a wide variety of activities, including games, that will greatly improve their ability to retain the required skills and knowledge necessary for the exam. It will also be useful beyond the exam and enable you to know that whatever the result, the learning period will have been time well spent.

Many old and new pencil and paper games, puzzles and skill challenges are included. Along side this, a large section of over 300 review questions, a Maths terminology glossary, as well as an answer key have been provided.

We hope that *The Big 11+ Maths Play Book* will be a useful resource in exam preparation.

Elizabeth Judge
The Armadillo's Pillow Ltd

How to use this book

What you will need: a six-sided die, and scissors. If you do not have any dice, you could alternately use your smartphone or computer to utilise one of the many online number generators, such as *random.org*, which has a free dice roller simulator. One of the exercises requires a protractor. Although the exams generally do not require a protractor, it does help with understanding of angle and line measurement. For the game of Shapes & Symmetry Bingo, anything from coins to squares of paper can be used.

~

This book provides 47 different activities, arranged to provide a variation through games, puzzles, cartoons, exercises and review questions that will effectively reinforce skills and knowledge. By going through these sections, you should be able to identify areas where you child needs additional study.

The activities may be used in any order, although the *Play Squares/Noughts and Crosses* section should be used as revision when closer to the exam. There are over 300 review questions organised by important 11+ topics — algebra, angles, data & graphs, direction, factors, fractions, the four operations, mean/median/mode, perimeter & area, probability, ratios, sequences, special numbers, symmetry, time, maths vocabulary, 3D and 2D shapes.

The glossary has been included to quickly review key Eleven Plus Maths terms and fundamental concepts.

The opportunity to photocopy allows your child to revisit the themes through games and puzzles as often as they wish.

Special Numbers

For the eleven plus exam there are certain types of numbers that you need to know. Sometimes, you will be asked specifically about these number types, whilst at other times, you will need to recognise their importance.

Square Numbers

These are the result of any two identical whole numbers multiplied together

Examples: $2 \times 2 = 4$ $6 \times 6 = 36$ $11 \times 11 = 121$

It is worth memorising these numbers up to 144 (12×12). The first twelve square numbers are **1, 4, 9, 16, 25, 36, 49, 64, 81, 100, 121, 144**

Cube Numbers

In this case, three identical numbers are multiplied, as would be necessary to discover the volume of a cube. (length x height x depth)

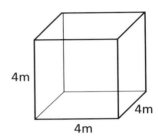

$$4 \times 4 \times 4 = 64m^3$$

It is worth learning these numbers up to and including 125 ($5 \times 5 \times 5$), in order to recognise them easily. The first five cube numbers are **1, 8, 27, 64, 125**

Triangular Numbers

A triangular number is the number of objects (or dots) that can form an equilateral triangle.

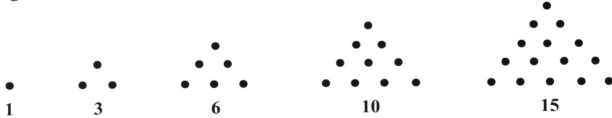

You should learn and remember these: **1, 3, 6, 10, 15** (see a pattern?)

Prime Numbers

These numbers are only divisible by 1 and themselves. Note that the number 1 is **<u>not</u>** accepted as a prime number. In learning these, it is often useful to think 'Is the number the answer to one of the times tables that I have learnt at school?'

The first eight prime numbers are: **2, 3, 5, 7, 11, 13, 17, 19**

Prime Position

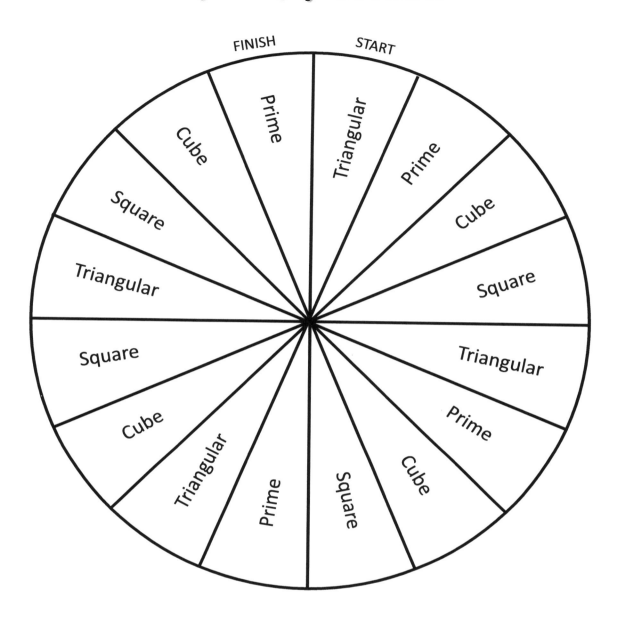

Rules: Both players start at the top of the wheel in the Triangular section, and travel clockwise around. Players take turns rolling two dice, or roll a single die twice. **The player can decide whether to add or multiply the numbers together**.

If the player rolls a number that is a prime, cube, square, or a triangular number, then they move clockwise to the next space around the wheel that matches the type of number rolled.

For example: Roll a 3 and a 5. The player can choose either 8 (cube) or 15 (triangular) as the number. Move clockwise around the wheel to the next sector marked 'cube' or 'triangular,' depending on which the player chooses. Then the next player takes a turn.

Do not go past the last 'Prime' section where you see 'Finish.' Stay on the last section until you can land in this final position.

To win the game, you must roll a prime number and land on the last section marked 'Finish.' It is often fun to play this game three times, with the 'best of 3' being the overall winner.

The Percentage Increase Game

This game has been created to help you improve your ability with increasing and decreasing amounts by percentages. As you know, percentages are simply a way of expressing part of an amount out of 100.

For this game, you will need a six-sided die, and a pencil and paper. Players start at the top of the board and get £200. Write down this amount, as you will gradually gain and lose money throughout your journey to the finish.

Roll the die once and move the number of spaces indicated. If you land on a space that increases by a percentage, then add that amount to your total.

Your total: £200

Land on space – Bonus increase 10%

10% of 200 = 20

New total: £220

Likewise, if you land on a space where you have to decrease by a percentage, then subtract that amount from your total.

Your total: £220

Land on space – Rent increase Pay 5%

5% of 220 = £11

New total: £209

You may also earn or spend money if you land on other spaces.

Round to the nearest £1 each turn.

The goal is to reach the 'Finish' space and still have money left over. If you are playing with another player, see who has the most money left over at the end. Add £50 to the total of the player who finishes first.

If you end up losing all of your money (not likely), then start over at the beginning with £200.

The Percentage Increase Game

START with £200

Buy a hat
Pay £10

Eat at a Restaurant
Pay £10

Bonus
Increase 10%

Buy a coat
Pay £15

GO BACK 3 SPACES

Bonus
Increase 10%

Sell Old Games
Earn £10

Lottery win
Increase 10%

GO BACK 3 SPACES

Donate
Give 10% of your money to charity

Buy a book
Pay £10

Tax
Pay 10%

Clean the Garage
Earn £20

Weekend
No charge

Rent Increase
Pay 5%

GO BACK 5 SPACES

Pay Rise
Increase 15%

Rent Increase
Pay 10%

Tax
Pay 10%

Create a Website
Earn £100

Bank Holiday
No charge

Bonus
Increase 10%

Sell Car
Earn £200

New Job
Increase 20%

GO BACK 6 SPACES

Bake Sale
Earn £15

Tax
Pay 10%

Pay Rise
Increase 10%

Bank Holiday
No charge

Bonus
Increase 10%

New Job
Increase 10%

Day at the park

Birthday Present
Earn £20

Tax
Pay 10%

Lost wallet
Lose £20

Tax
Pay 10%

GO BACK 5 SPACES

FINISH
earn £50 if you finish first

ROMAN NUMERALS

Roman numerals are the numbers that were used in ancient Rome. We still see and use them sometimes today, and you should remember the symbols for the following values:

Numeral	I	V	X	L	C	D	M
Value	1	5	10	50	100	500	1000

Other numbers are then made by calculating symbol combinations. The numbers are usually written in order, from left to right. It is important to remember that you will never have more than three of the same Roman numerals together. Instead, you use subtraction where a smaller number is placed in front of a larger number, as in these cases:

> I before V and X   example: IV (4) and IX (9)
>
> X before L and C   example: XL (40) and XC (90)
>
> C before D and M   example: CD (400) and CM (900)

One way to remember the Roman numerals in order would be to think of a saying that includes them all. For example:

My
Dog
Clearly
Likes
(e)**X**tra
Vitamins
Immensely

I
Value
(e)**X**tra
Long
Club
Dance
Marathons

You will probably run into a Roman numeral or two during the exam. So let's practise with a game.

What do you call a number that can't stop moving? **A Roamin' Numeral!**

12

THE ROMAN NUMERAL GAME

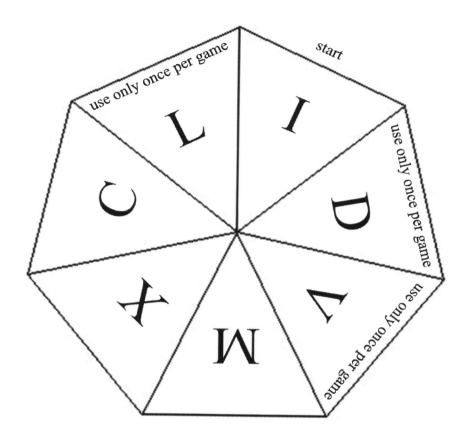

In this game, you can cut out the shape above to use as a spinner, or use a six-sided die. You will also need a pencil and paper to write down your numerals.

If using a die, the first player will roll a number, and advance from 'I' going clockwise. Write down the Roman Numeral that you land on. Continue rolling for three more goes, when you will have **four** Roman numerals.

Note – The Roman numerals V, L, and D can only be used once per game. Although not likely, do not use I, X, C, M more than 3 times per game. Roll again and get a different numeral if you do.

Arrange the symbols into the greatest number you can make using the Roman numeral rules. (If using the spinner, simply spin four times, and collect the letters landed on to play)

Player two then goes, starting from 'I'. Collecting four symbols, they arrange them into the greatest number possible. The player with the largest number wins the game. It is often fun to play this game three times, with the 'best of 3' being the overall winner.

The Venn Diagram Game

Venn Diagrams are used to visually organise sets of information, so you can easily see the relationships among sets.

For this game, you need 3 dice, or one die that you roll three times! Add up the total of the three dice, and decide where that number fits on the Venn Diagram (see opposite page).

Scoring:

- If the number belongs in 2 sets: 5 points
- If the number belongs in only one set: 2 points
- If the number is not in any set: minus 10 points (-10)
- If the number belongs in all 3 sets: 10 points (Game 2 only)

The first player to 30 points wins.

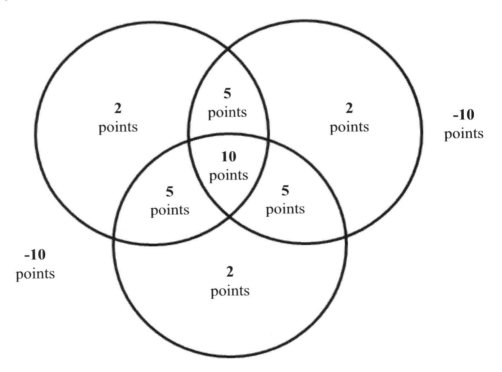

There are two different games to play.

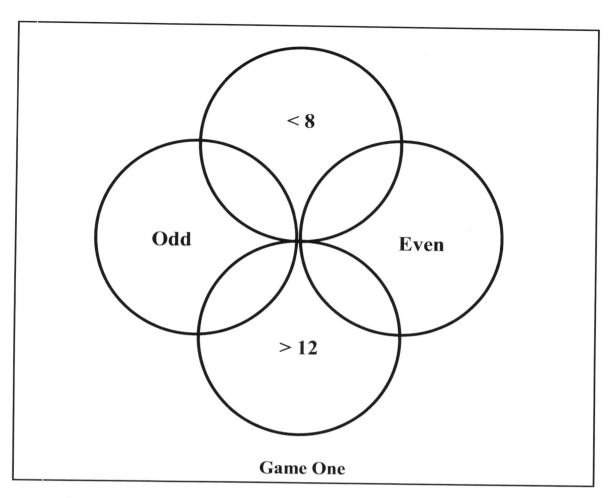

Game One

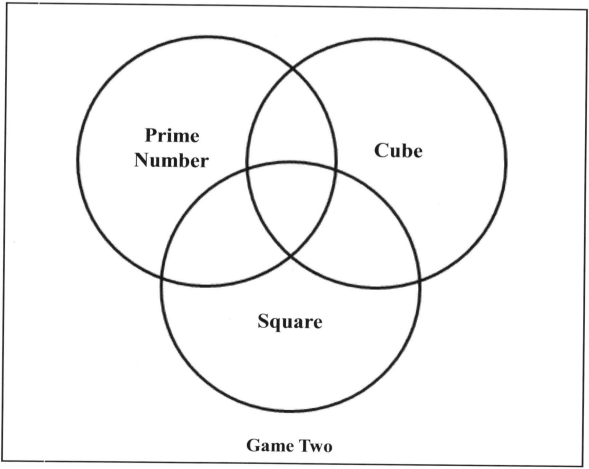

Game Two

Guesstimate

It is essential that you are able to make realistic estimates in the exam. Therefore we have designed this game to help you think about measurements that might come in useful later on.

In this game, shuffle the Guesstimate cards and place them in a pile with the 'Guesstimate' side up. The first player starts by taking a card, without turning it over. Both players must guess the **<u>measure</u>**. The player who is closest will keep the card and win that round.

The first player to win 6 rounds is the game winner, or you can play until you run out of cards.

Units used for length and weight are always **metric**, and the measures are **averages**.

Guesstimate Weight of an adult African elephant in kilograms	**Guesstimate** Height of a giant sunflower in metres
Guesstimate Speed of a snail in metres per second or kilometres per hour	**Guesstimate** Temperature of a volcano in Celsius
Guesstimate Capacity (volume) in litres of a 25m length swimming pool	**Guesstimate** Length of a Pop song in minutes and seconds
Guesstimate Distance from London to Edinburgh in kilometres	**Guesstimate** Temperature of the Arctic in winter in Celsius
Guesstimate Capacity (volume) of a water balloon in millilitres	**Guesstimate** Length of a man's nose in centimetres
Guesstimate Time to bake a two-layer cake in minutes	**Guesstimate** Weight of an orange in grams

3 m	5,443 kg
1,300° C	.047 km/h or 0.013 m/sec
3 min 30 sec	375,000 litres
-34° C	648 km
5.8 cm	45 ml
140 g	30 min

Guesstimate	**Guesstimate**
Length in time of a plane journey from London to New York in hours and minutes	Height of a door in millimetres
Guesstimate	**Guesstimate**
Weight of a laptop computer in kilograms	Area of a football pitch in metres squared
Guesstimate	**Guesstimate**
Surface area of a bath towel (both sides) in metres squared	Area of a typical house in the U.K. in metres squared
Guesstimate	**Guesstimate**
Length of a Burmese python in metres	Length of a film in hours and minutes
Guesstimate	**Guesstimate**
Max speed of a cheetah in kilometres per hour	Weight of a hedgehog in grams
Guesstimate	**Guesstimate**
Weight of a butterfly in grams	Length of a female great white shark in metres

1981 mm	7 hrs 45 min
7,140 m²	2.3 kg
85 m²	4 m²
90 min or $1\frac{1}{2}$ hours	7 m
400 g	93 km/h
5.5 m	0.5 g

Decimal Dance

This is a game where you will practise moving the appropriate number of places whilst multiplying or dividing.

Using a regular six-sided die, players take turns rolling and then moving the decimal either to the left or the right, depending on the roll.

Roll 1   divide by one thousand (÷1000)
Roll 2   multiply by ten (x10)
Roll 3   divide by one hundred (÷100)
Roll 4   multiply by one thousand (x1000)
Roll 5   divide by ten (÷10)
Roll 6   multiply by one hundred (x100)

Use the decimal lines below for each player. Start at the middle.

The winner is the player that has the highest number after ten turns. You may want to keep your pen or pencil in position between turns.

Player One:

start

6 5 0 4 5 1 3 5 6 9 0 . 7 2 4 6 8 3 2 8 4 1 5

Player Two:

start

6 5 0 4 5 1 3 5 6 9 0 . 7 2 4 6 8 3 2 8 4 1 5

Fun Factors & Merry Multiples

How fast are you with factors and multiples?

This is a game for two players. The first player starts the game by choosing an **<u>even</u>** number from the game board, and crosses it out. The second player chooses a number that is a **factor** or **multiple** of the number player 1 chose.

Player 1 now must choose a number that is a factor of the number that player 2 has just crossed off. The game continues, with each player selecting a number that is a factor or multiple of the previous number chosen.

A player loses when they can no longer find a factor or multiple of the last number selected.

You can play the shorter version (numbers 1 – 50) or the longer version (1 – 100).

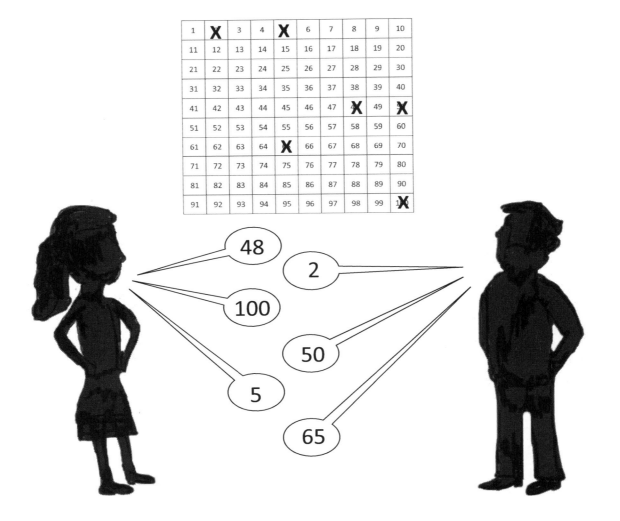

Fun Factors & Merry Multiples

1	2	3	4	5	6	7	8	9	10
11	12	13	14	15	16	17	18	19	20
21	22	23	24	25	26	27	28	29	30
31	32	33	34	35	36	37	38	39	40
41	42	43	44	45	46	47	48	49	50

Shorter Game (1-50)

1	2	3	4	5	6	7	8	9	10
11	12	13	14	15	16	17	18	19	20
21	22	23	24	25	26	27	28	29	30
31	32	33	34	35	36	37	38	39	40
41	42	43	44	45	46	47	48	49	50
51	52	53	54	55	56	57	58	59	60
61	62	63	64	65	66	67	68	69	70
71	72	73	74	75	76	77	78	79	80
81	82	83	84	85	86	87	88	89	90
91	92	93	94	95	96	97	98	99	100

Longer Game (1-100)

In Reflection

For the exercises below, draw the reflectional (mirror) image of each shape based on the axis indicated.

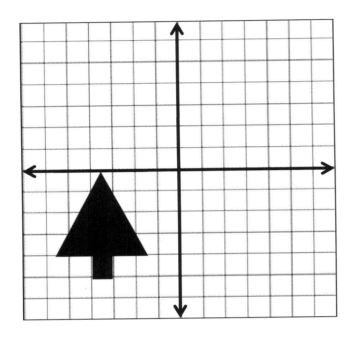

1) The Tree
   x-axis

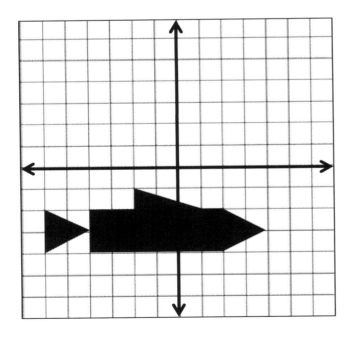

2) The Bug
   y-axis

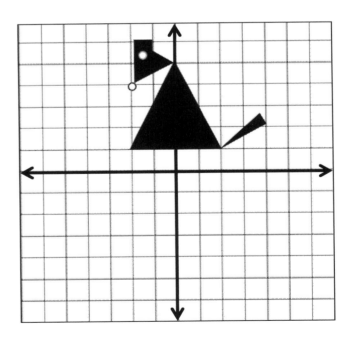

3) The Fish
   x-axis

4) The Dog
   x-axis

Crack the Codes

Try to work out what each symbol's value is worth. Each symbol will represent a number from 1 to 12. Four of the answers have been provided to give you a head start.

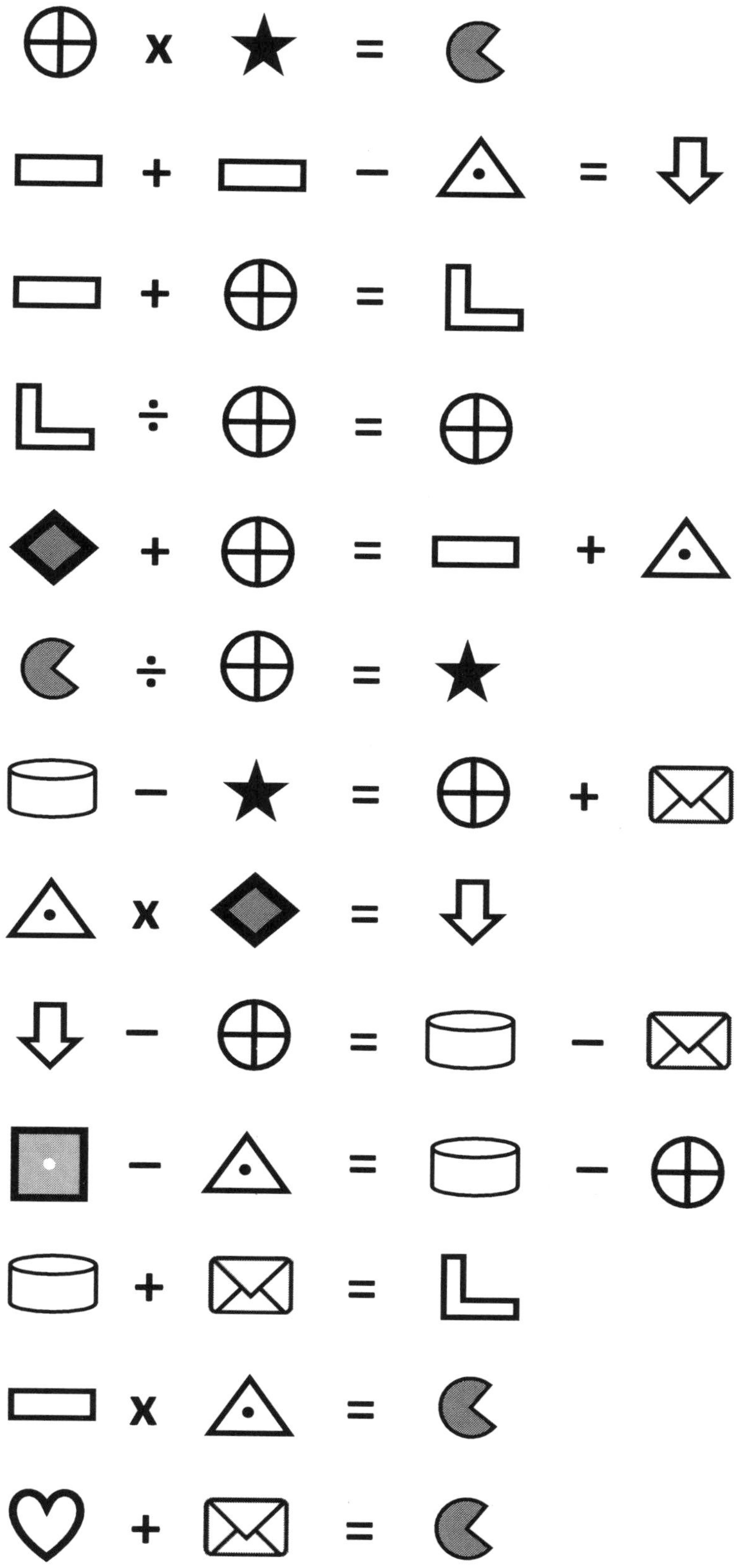

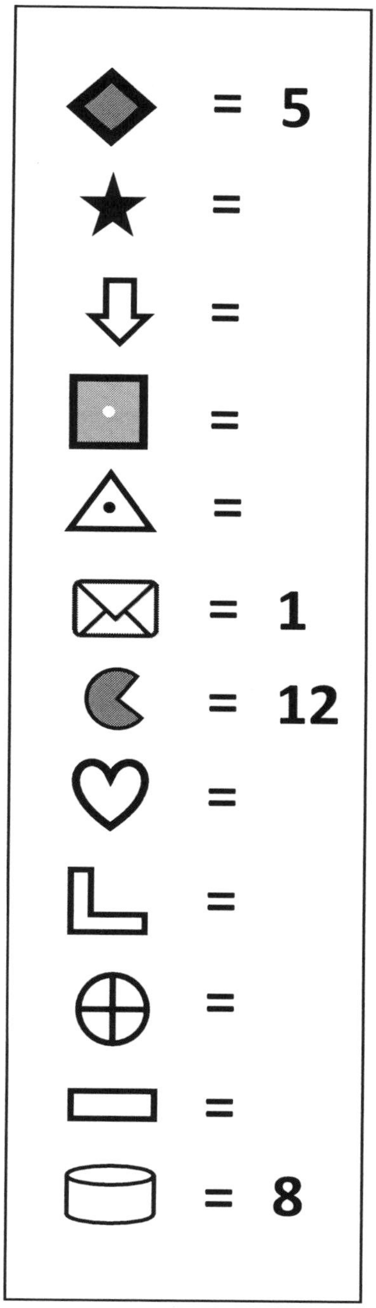

⊕ x ★ = ◖ (pac-man)

▭ + ▭ − △ = ⇩

▭ + ⊕ = ∟

∟ ÷ ⊕ = ⊕

◆ + ⊕ = ▭ + △

◖ ÷ ⊕ = ★

⬭ − ★ = ⊕ + ✉

△ x ◆ = ⇩

⇩ − ⊕ = ⬭ − ✉

▣ − △ = ⬭ − ⊕

⬭ + ✉ = ∟

▭ x △ = ◖

♡ + ✉ = ◖

◆	=	5
★	=	
⇩	=	
▣	=	
△	=	
✉	=	1
◖	=	12
♡	=	
∟	=	
⊕	=	
▭	=	
⬭	=	8

25

Fractions Snap!

This is a game that is all about recognising fractions that are of equal value. For example:

$$\frac{1}{2} = \frac{2}{4} \qquad \frac{2}{3} = \frac{12}{18} \qquad \frac{1}{3} = \frac{3}{9} \qquad \frac{3}{4} = \frac{6}{8}$$

Cut out the cards on the following pages. All cards should be shuffled and placed in a central pile face down. The players take turns lifting up a card, placing it face up so that all can see, creating a row of cards.

If a card is lifted from the main stack of cards, that is the same value as one of any of the cards already lifted, the first player to say 'Snap!' gets to keep that pair of cards.

Note that there are 12 sets of 4 different fractions that have the same value.

The winner is the player with the most pairs of cards after all cards have been lifted.

$\dfrac{1}{4}$	$\dfrac{2}{8}$	$\dfrac{3}{12}$	$\dfrac{4}{16}$
$\dfrac{1}{2}$	$\dfrac{5}{10}$	$\dfrac{7}{14}$	$\dfrac{9}{18}$
$\dfrac{3}{4}$	$\dfrac{6}{8}$	$\dfrac{9}{12}$	$\dfrac{15}{20}$
$\dfrac{2}{3}$	$\dfrac{6}{9}$	$\dfrac{12}{18}$	$\dfrac{20}{30}$
$\dfrac{4}{5}$	$\dfrac{8}{10}$	$\dfrac{12}{15}$	$\dfrac{16}{20}$
$\dfrac{1}{8}$	$\dfrac{2}{16}$	$\dfrac{3}{24}$	$\dfrac{4}{32}$

Fractions Snap!	**Fractions Snap!**	**Fractions Snap!**	**Fractions Snap!**
Fractions Snap!	**Fractions Snap!**	**Fractions Snap!**	**Fractions Snap!**
Fractions Snap!	**Fractions Snap!**	**Fractions Snap!**	**Fractions Snap!**
Fractions Snap!	**Fractions Snap!**	**Fractions Snap!**	**Fractions Snap!**
Fractions Snap!	**Fractions Snap!**	**Fractions Snap!**	**Fractions Snap!**
Fractions Snap!	**Fractions Snap!**	**Fractions Snap!**	**Fractions Snap!**

$\dfrac{1}{7}$	$\dfrac{2}{14}$	$\dfrac{3}{21}$	$\dfrac{5}{35}$
$\dfrac{5}{9}$	$\dfrac{10}{18}$	$\dfrac{20}{36}$	$\dfrac{25}{45}$
$\dfrac{3}{8}$	$\dfrac{6}{16}$	$\dfrac{15}{40}$	$\dfrac{21}{56}$
$\dfrac{5}{6}$	$\dfrac{10}{12}$	$\dfrac{15}{18}$	$\dfrac{20}{24}$
$\dfrac{1}{12}$	$\dfrac{4}{48}$	$\dfrac{6}{72}$	$\dfrac{7}{84}$
$\dfrac{5}{4}$	$1\dfrac{1}{4}$	$\dfrac{10}{8}$	$1\dfrac{4}{16}$

Fractions Snap!	**Fractions Snap!**	**Fractions Snap!**	**Fractions Snap!**
Fractions Snap!	**Fractions Snap!**	**Fractions Snap!**	**Fractions Snap!**
Fractions Snap!	**Fractions Snap!**	**Fractions Snap!**	**Fractions Snap!**
Fractions Snap!	**Fractions Snap!**	**Fractions Snap!**	**Fractions Snap!**
Fractions Snap!	**Fractions Snap!**	**Fractions Snap!**	**Fractions Snap!**
Fractions Snap!	**Fractions Snap!**	**Fractions Snap!**	**Fractions Snap!**

Mystery Wheels

Each of the wheels below are missing a number. Can you figure out what the missing number should be? Look for patterns – the direction may not always be clockwise. Most are sequences, but you can never be too sure. Use your mathematical reasoning to solve the mystery.

Let's get warmed up with some easy ones...

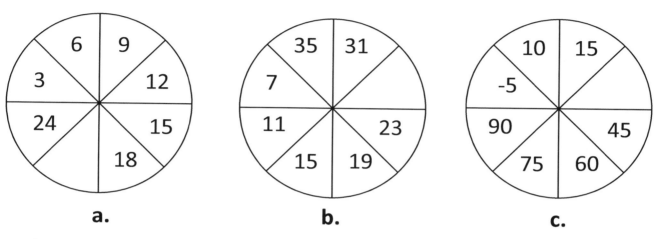

a.   **b.**   **c.**

Now they get a little harder...

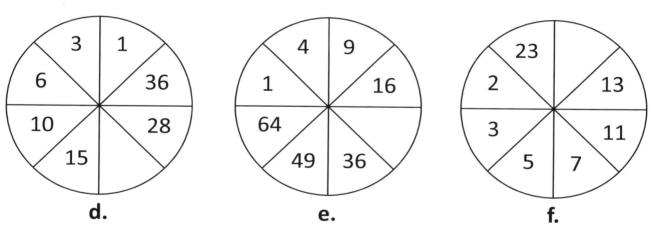

d.   **e.**   **f.**

Finally the expert level... you can do it!

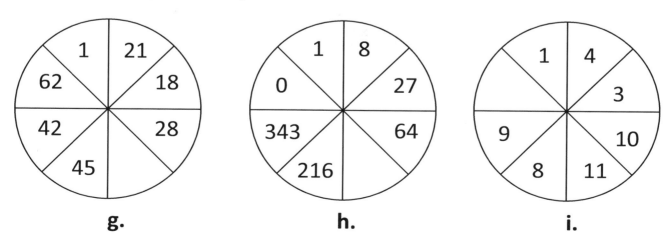

g.   **h.**   **i.**

THE SECRET LIFE OF NUMBERS

7 is even – when you take away the 's'

Generations of Fractions

The BODMAS monster

The Secret Life of Numbers

The great operators debate

Square Dance

Ice Cubes

Round House

Rounding numbers can be useful, especially when trying to estimate an answer involving very large numbers. Remember the trick for rounding up or down – if the next digit after the number you are rounding to is:

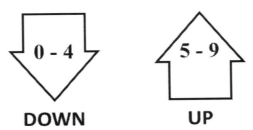

Then round -   **DOWN**   **UP**

Example: 400,357 rounded to the nearest hundred = 400,400
314,279 rounded to the nearest ten thousand = 310,000

Look carefully at the place value of the number you are rounding.

The Round House Game

This is a game for two players, using two 6-sided dice (or rolling the same die twice!).

Players will roll the dice and create a two digit number they must round to the nearest ten. It is up to the player to choose which number they create, if the numbers are different. For example, a 2 and a 6 roll could be either 62 or 26.

Using the game circles, put your initials in one half of the number you roll. (Note – rolling two sixes – 66 – does not score)

The player who gets two initials first in one circle completes it, therefore winning that circle.

Players will continue and the first player to win four of the circles wins the game. Example: player 'L' wins

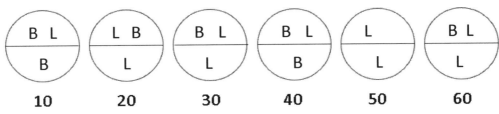

Round House Game 1

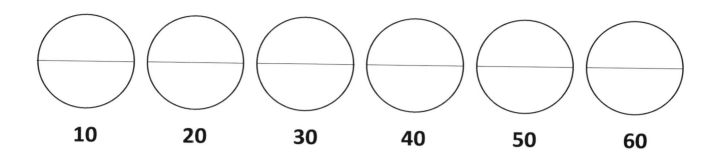

Round House Game 2

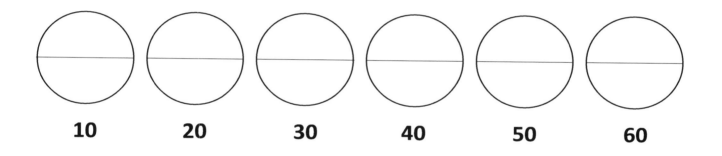

Round House Game 3

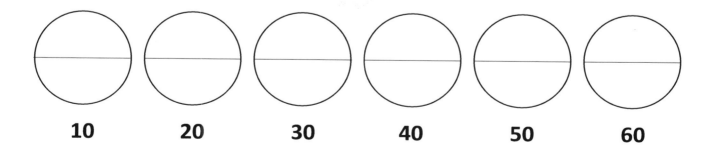

Missing Operators

In these exercises, you will need to think differently and look at the numbers to determine the operations that are missing.

Fill in the blanks for each question by inserting a mathematical operation – addition (+), subtract (-), multiplication (x), or division (÷). **You can only use each operation only once per question**.

Note: Some of the brackets may not be necessary. The first question has been done as an example.

$$(5 \times 1) \div 5 + 5 = 6$$

(5 X 5 =5)   5 ÷ 5 =1   1 + 5 =6

① (7 ☐ 2) ☐ 3 = 3

② (1 ☐ 4) ☐ 2 = 6

③ (5 ☐ 5) ☐ 5 = 50

④ (8 ☐ 5) ☐ 6 = 18

(5) | 12 | | 2 | | 6 | = | 30 |

(6) (| 25 | | 4 |) | | 7 | = | 3 |

(7) | 100 | | 10 | | 4 | = | 6 |

(8) (| 4 | | 5 |) | | 3 | = | 27 |

(9) | 3 | | (| 7 | | 5 |) | | 1 | = | 7 |

Challenge Questions

(10) (| 35 | | 7 |) | | 3 | | (| 2 | | 3 |) | = | 8 |

(2 possible answers)

(11) (| 15 | | 11 |) | | 3 | | (| 2 | | 4 |) | = | 2 |

(12) (| 6 | | 6 |) | | 2 | | 8 | | 4 | = | 14 |

THE ANGLER

The angler likes to go fishing for some interesting angles. Let's see what he finds.

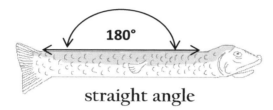

straight angle

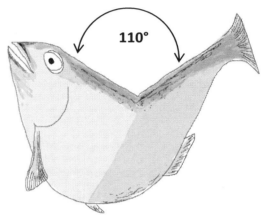

An obtuse angle
(greater than 90° but less than 180°)

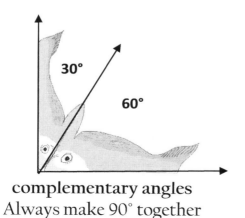

X angle
This rare fish has fins that form **opposite angles** which are equal

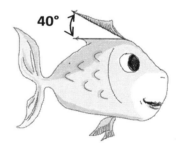

Acute angle
(less than 90° - isn't he cute?)

complementary angles
Always make 90° together

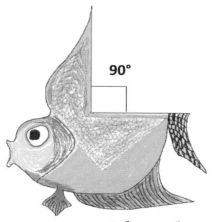

right angle

38

Escape the Unbearable

Bearings are used to describe the position of things or places by measuring the clockwise angle of the point, relative to North. Bearings are measured as 3-digit numbers. For example the major directions are:

North - 000°
East - 090°
South - 180°
West - 270°

For the game 'Escape the Unbearable' you will need two six-sided dice, a protractor, ruler and pencil. Use the game map on the opposite page and cut out the game cards.

The first player starts by drawing one of the game direction cards, which shows the direction to travel. They then roll the dice, and that will be the distance to travel (in centimetres). Start at the middle of the game board. After moving, mark your spot on the board with a dot and your initial. Then the next player will take a turn.

If you go off the board (outside of the rectangular playing area), or land in the *Forbidden Zone*, *Trapezium Trap* or *The Bermuda Triangle* then you must return to the 'Start' position.

The player who is **furthest** from the starting position after 8 turns (there are 16 cards, 8 per player) is the winner.

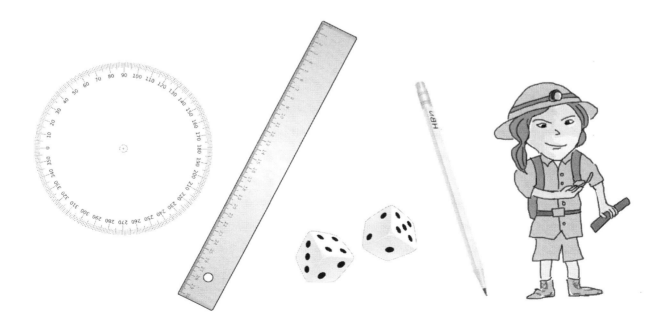

Forbidden Zone

Trapezium Trap

start here

Forbidden Zone

The Bermuda Triangle

045°	270°
090°	025°
180°	015°
110°	075°
020°	180°
135°	270°
045°	050°
000°	185°

Escape the Unbearable Direction Card	Escape the Unbearable Direction Card
Escape the Unbearable Direction Card	Escape the Unbearable Direction Card
Escape the Unbearable Direction Card	Escape the Unbearable Direction Card
Escape the Unbearable Direction Card	Escape the Unbearable Direction Card
Escape the Unbearable Direction Card	Escape the Unbearable Direction Card
Escape the Unbearable Direction Card	Escape the Unbearable Direction Card
Escape the Unbearable Direction Card	Escape the Unbearable Direction Card
Escape the Unbearable Direction Card	Escape the Unbearable Direction Card

Sneaky Sequences

The key to sequences is to be able to spot **patterns** or **rules** that will help you to work out the missing numbers. Usually the pattern is connected with addition, subtraction, multiplication or division.

Start with a sequence by looking at the differences between numbers:

Some may even have a combination of operations

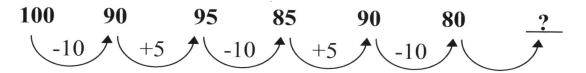

Do you remember what this kind of sequence is called?

?   5   8   13   21   34   ?

The rule is to add together the previous two numbers to get the next number in the sequence. This is called a **Fibonacci Sequence**. So we can work out that the first number should be 3 $(3 + 5 = 8)$ and the last number should be 55 $(21 + 34 = 55)$

TIPS FOR SOLVING SEQUENCE QUESTIONS

- Always check for square or cube numbers first
- Be ready to use the four operations (add, subtract, multiply or divide) one or more times
- Work with the line from right to left if this is easier
- Seeing a 'skip' pattern that leap frogs in a regular pattern can help
- Write above or below the numbers – anything that helps
- If the answer is not apparent, perhaps you need to check for triangular or prime numbers
- Short sequences are not necessarily easier
- Be prepared for negative numbers

Now try to solve the missing number in these sneaky sequences on your own:

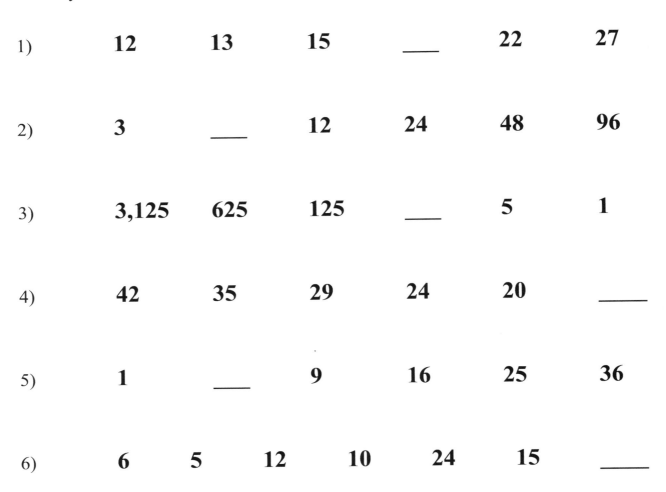

1)   12   13   15   ___   22   27

2)   3   ___   12   24   48   96

3)   3,125   625   125   ___   5   1

4)   42   35   29   24   20   ___

5)   1   ___   9   16   25   36

6)   6   5   12   10   24   15   ___

Worded Sequence Questions – Sequences can also appear as part of a worded Maths problem.

7)   Meg and Shauna were making hamburgers. They found they could make 10 in one hour, 12 in the next hour, and 14 in the following hour. How many should they have made in total after four hours (if they increased output at the same rate)?

8)   Giovanni starts a website and gets 20 emails on a Monday. If the amount of emails he receives doubles each day, how many will he receive on Friday?

9)   Eva spends an average 1260 minutes each week playing video games. Her mum wants her to reduce the amount of time spent each week by an hour and 20 minutes. How many weeks will it take her to get to under 15 hours?

10) The lottery prize is £10.2 million in the first week, then £16.2 million in week 2, £14.2 million in week 3, £20.2 million in week 4, £18.2 million in week 5. What will be the prize in week 10 if this pattern continues?

11) Observe the sequence pattern of squares and diamonds.

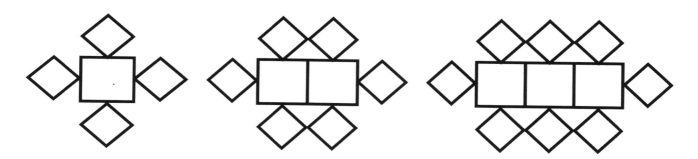

How many diamonds would there be in a pattern with 6 squares? _____

How many diamonds would there be in a pattern with 12 squares? _____

12) What is the missing section in the grid below?

4	6	5	6
1		2	
3	5		5
4	6	5	

see any patterns?

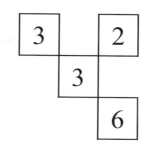

3		4
	3	
		6

a.

2		3
	4	
		5

b.

3		2
	3	
		6

c.

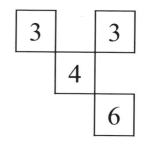

3		3
	4	
		6

d.

45

Shapes & Symmetry
BINGO

Bingo is a traditional game where players have a mat and mark off a square for each matching number called at random. The goal is get a complete row, column, or diagonal before the other players.

For the *Shapes & Symmetry BINGO*, start by cutting out the game cards and giving each player a mat. Two players then take turns answering questions on the game cards. Players must work out the answer, and then find the correct response on their mat. Cover your square with a coin or other similar marker.

Keep playing until you have one of the following winning mats:

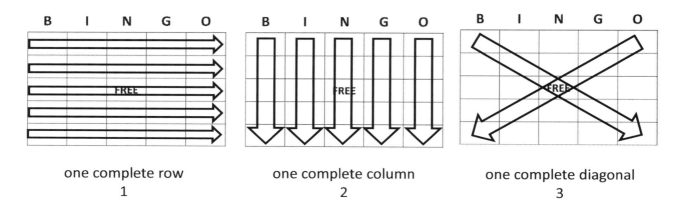

one complete row   one complete column   one complete diagonal
1   2   3

Note that the middle square in the N column is free, which means that you do not need to answer a question to use that square. If you need to review shapes and symmetry terms, check out the glossary on page 145.

The answers to the Bingo questions are in the Answer Key as well.

Shapes & Symmetry **BINGO**	*Shapes & Symmetry* **BINGO**
Shapes & Symmetry **BINGO**	*Shapes & Symmetry* **BINGO**
Shapes & Symmetry **BINGO**	*Shapes & Symmetry* **BINGO**
Shapes & Symmetry **BINGO**	*Shapes & Symmetry* **BINGO**
Shapes & Symmetry **BINGO**	*Shapes & Symmetry* **BINGO**
Shapes & Symmetry **BINGO**	*Shapes & Symmetry* **BINGO**

What is a six-sided polygon called?	What shape has fewer lines of reflectional symmetry: An equilateral triangle, or a rhombus?
What is an eight-sided polygon called?	What is another word for having the same shape and size?
What is the name of a shape that has 3 equal angles and 3 lines of reflectional symmetry?	What is the number of edges in a cuboid minus the number of its vertices?
What are the number of faces of a pentagonal prism?	When two lines cross at a right angle, what can they be called?
Find the 3D shape on your card that has no vertices	What is the number of lines of reflectional symmetry in a parallelogram, that is not a rhombus or a square?
What is the measure of each angle in an equilateral triangle?	Does a parallelogram (that is not a square) have an order of rotational symmetry of 2?

Shapes & Symmetry **BINGO**	*Shapes & Symmetry* **BINGO**
Shapes & Symmetry **BINGO**	*Shapes & Symmetry* **BINGO**
Shapes & Symmetry **BINGO**	*Shapes & Symmetry* **BINGO**
Shapes & Symmetry **BINGO**	*Shapes & Symmetry* **BINGO**
Shapes & Symmetry **BINGO**	*Shapes & Symmetry* **BINGO**
Shapes & Symmetry **BINGO**	*Shapes & Symmetry* **BINGO**

What is the order of rotational symmetry of a kite?	When an isosceles triangle has one angle that equals 90°, what is the size of each of the other two angles?
What is the name of a 2D pattern, that can be folded to create a 3D shape?	What is the name of two lines, that are always the same distance apart?
A rectangle has four angles that all measure _____ degrees	What is a line called, that goes from one side of a circle to the other, and passes through the centre?
How many vertices does a cuboid have?	What is the number of vertices in a triangular prism?
Does an isosceles triangle always have a 90° angle?	What is a 3-dimensional solid which consists of a collection of polygons, usually joined at their edges?
How many equal angles does an isosceles triangle have?	What is the name of a triangle that has unequal sides?

BINGO

B	I	N	G	O
Hexagon	Polyhedron	0	perpendicular	4
90°	Yes	6	Octagon	2
7	Scalene	**FREE**	Rhombus	Parallel
Equilateral Triangle	60°	Net	1	Cylinder
Congruent	8	Diameter	45°	No

Player One Mat

BINGO

B	I	N	G	O
1	Rhombus	Equilateral Triangle	Cylinder	Yes
No	6	0	Net	7
Octagon	8	**FREE**	Polyhedron	Diameter
45°	Hexagon	2	90°	Congruent
perpendicular	60°	Parallel	Scalene	4

Player Two Mat

The Probability Game

When two things happen

In this game, you will practise multiplying fractions to determine the probability of two independent events happening at the same time. (Note: Independent events are not connected, the probability of one has no effect on the other)

The first player takes **two** event cards from the set. They must compute the total probability of both events happening, by multiplying the fractions, and expressing the answer as a proper fraction.

For example:

The 1st card's probability is $\frac{1}{4}$ The 2nd card's probability is $\frac{1}{5}$

To find the probability of both events happening, we multiply the numerators together (1 x 1) and the denominators together (4 x 5). Therefore

The combined probability is $\frac{1}{20}$

If the player is correct they keep the cards and the next player goes. If the answer is incorrect, the player returns the cards to the bottom of the pile. The first player to win five rounds (10 cards) is the winner of the game.

Alternate game: Find the probability of either one or another independent events happening by adding the fractions together.

I come in second in the race $^1/_8$	I get heads when tossing a coin $^1/_2$
I pick a green counter from a bag $^5/_9$	Tomorrow it will rain $^2/_3$
I roll a six on a die $^1/_6$	My parents' new car will break down $^1/_{150}$
My birth month has 30 days $^1/_4$	I pick a vowel from the word 'chance' $^1/_3$
My dad's birthday is in the winter $^1/_4$	I win the raffle $^1/_{100}$
February will have only 28 days $^3/_4$	My entry wins the art competition $^2/_{15}$

Event Card	Event Card
Event Card	Event Card
Event Card	Event Card
Event Card	Event Card
Event Card	Event Card
Event Card	Event Card

The train is more than 10 minutes late $\frac{1}{5}$	I complete the test in under 45 minutes $\frac{1}{30}$
My drink costs more than my sandwich $\frac{1}{15}$	My bedroom will be tidy on Friday $\frac{1}{7}$
There will be a thunderstorm next week $\frac{3}{28}$	I will remember the day I was born $\frac{0}{0}$
The sun will set this evening $\frac{1}{1}$	I will swim this holiday $\frac{4}{9}$
I will have peas with dinner tonight $\frac{3}{7}$	I will pass my driving test this year $\frac{0}{0}$
England will win the World Cup $\frac{1}{14}$	I will have ice cream tonight $\frac{1}{5}$

Event Card	Event Card
Event Card	Event Card
Event Card	Event Card
Event Card	Event Card
Event Card	Event Card
Event Card	Event Card

DOWN ON THE RANGE

Down on the range, it's all about counting the cattle. We have our funny ways of keeping track of them. You should learn them too!

We call the difference between the youngest and the oldest the **range**!

65

48

48

63

240

50

6

Joey is **6** months old. He's the youngest

Betsy's the oldest. She's **240** months old. (That's old for a cow)

So the **range** is 234 months (240 – 6). Get it?

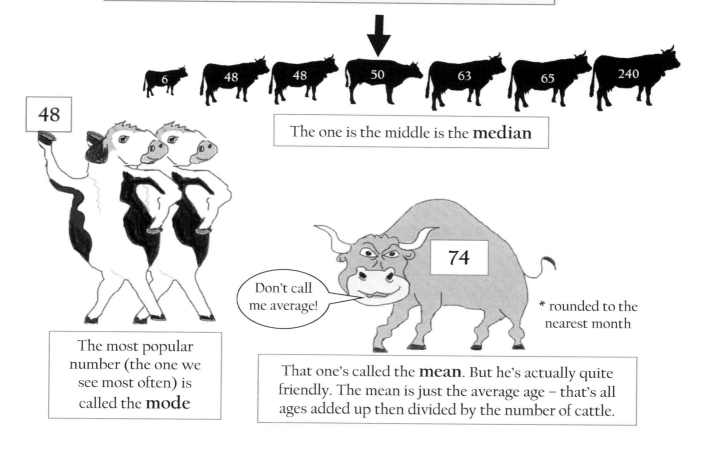

48

6 48 48 50 63 65 240

The one is the middle is the **median**

74

Don't call me average!

* rounded to the nearest month

The most popular number (the one we see most often) is called the **mode**

That one's called the **mean**. But he's actually quite friendly. The mean is just the average age – that's all ages added up then divided by the number of cattle.

I Really Mean It

In this game, we practise determining the mean, mode, median, and range of a set of numbers. You can play either alone, or with another player. Use the number cards and lay out a set of five cards at random.

The players will then write down the mean, mode, median, and range. Once they are done, they should announce 'I really mean it!' If they have all of the correct answers, they win the round. If they have any incorrect answers, the round goes to the opposing player.

The first player to win 5 rounds is the winner.

| 5 | 3 | 2 | 4 | 7 |

In the example above:

The **mean** is 4.2 $(21 \div 5)$

The **median** is 4 (ordering from the lowest to highest, 2, 3, **4**, 5, 7)

The **mode** is multimodal (If there are 3 or more numbers that appear most often in the set of numbers, the answer is multimodal. If there **2** numbers that appear most often, it is **bi**modal). In this case, all of the numbers appear the same amount of times.

The **range** is 5 $(7 - 2)$

I really mean it!

1	1	1	1
2	2	2	2
3	3	3	3
4	4	4	4
5	5	5	5
6	6	6	6
3	3	3	3
2	2	2	2
1	1	1	1
7	8	9	10

I really mean it	I really mean it	I really mean it	I really mean it
I really mean it	I really mean it	I really mean it	I really mean it
I really mean it	I really mean it	I really mean it	I really mean it
I really mean it	I really mean it	I really mean it	I really mean it
I really mean it	I really mean it	I really mean it	I really mean it
I really mean it	I really mean it	I really mean it	I really mean it
I really mean it	I really mean it	I really mean it	I really mean it
I really mean it	I really mean it	I really mean it	I really mean it
I really mean it	I really mean it	I really mean it	I really mean it
I really mean it	I really mean it	I really mean it	I really mean it

What Was the Question?

In this exercise, we turn the question around, providing an answer, and asking you to say what the question was! (Note: Some answers may have alternative but true questions, than those suggested in the Answer Key)

1) 360°
2) nonagon
3) rhombus
4) 0.125
5) cube
6) 180°
7) 0, 1, 1, 2, 3, 5, 8, 13
8) L
9) 1, 2, 3, 4, 6, 12
10) 60°
11) perimeter
12) 10,000 m
13) A reflex angle
14) 1, 3, 6, 10, 15, 21
15) heptagon
16) MLIX
17) 25
18) $\frac{1}{2}$ base X height
19) diameter
20) vertex
21) 1,000 ml
22) $\frac{3}{5}$
23) ratio
24) volume
25) factor

Symbol Addition

In this exercise you will try to determine the value of each symbol based on the sum of each row, column or diagonal as shown. The first problem has been done as an example

The sum of the three symbols in this column is 7

The sum of the three symbols in the diagonal is 5

The sum of the three symbols in this row is 4

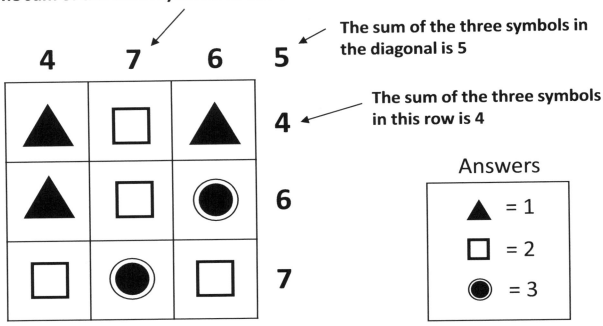

Answers

▲ = 1
□ = 2
◉ = 3

TIP for solving symbol addition: Trial and error can help.

1

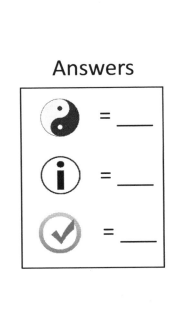

Answers

= ___

= ___

= ___

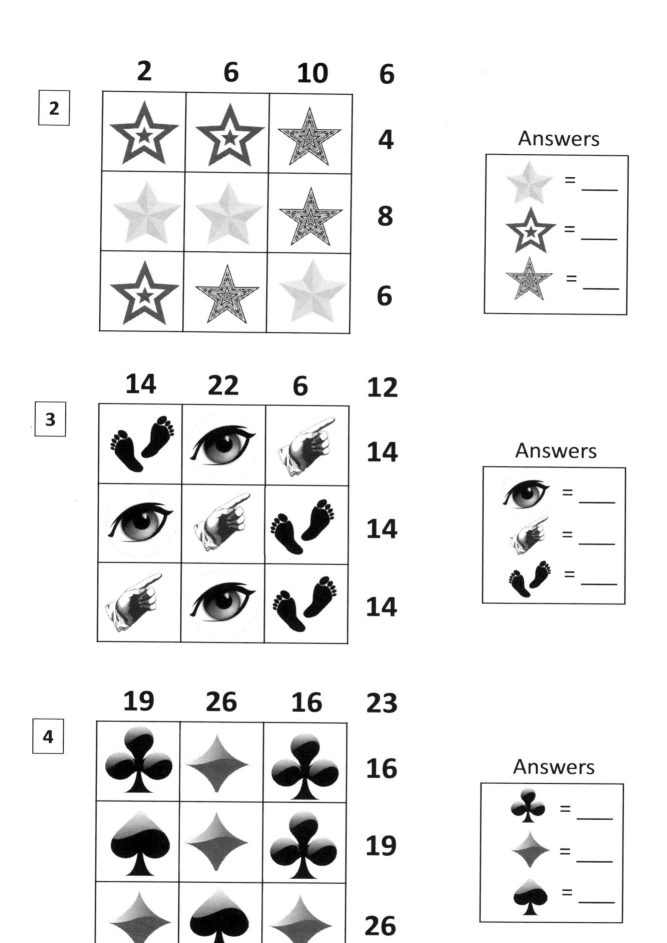

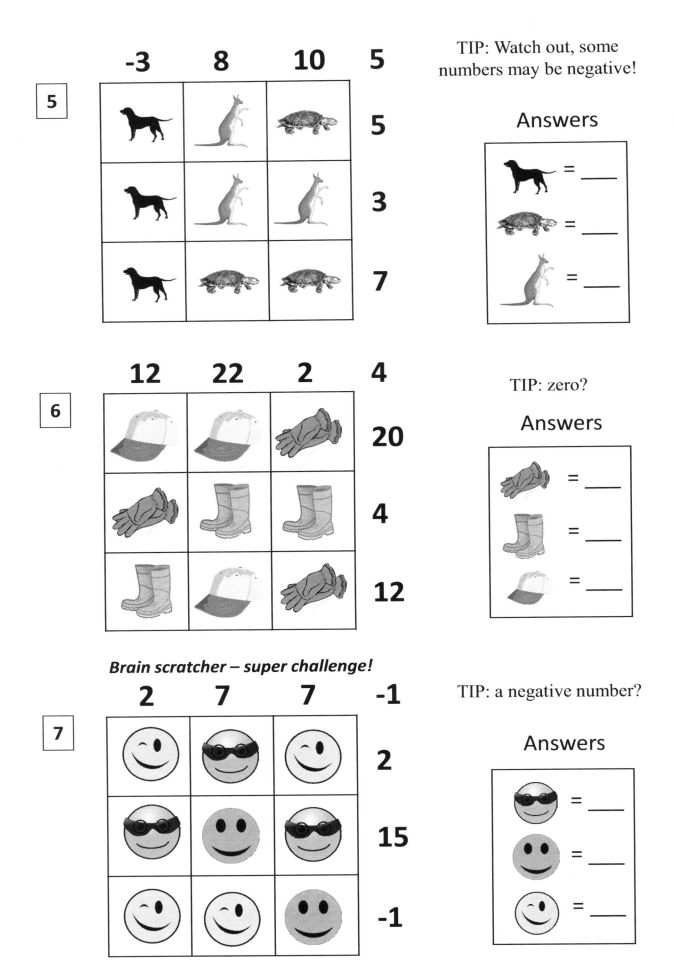

Square Master

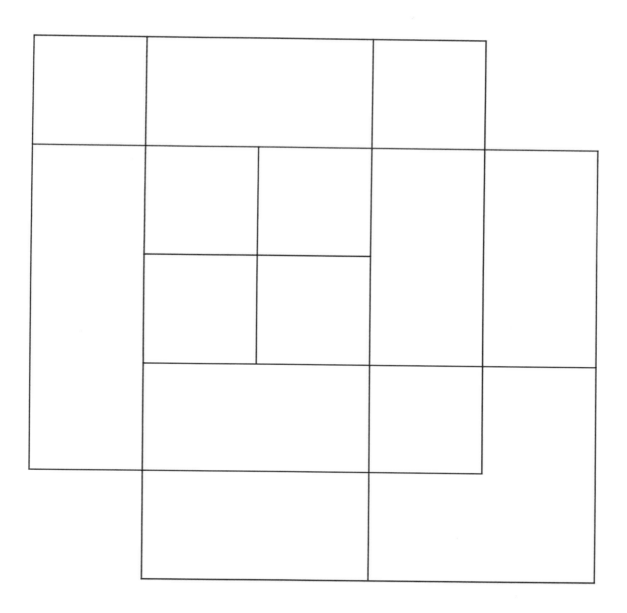

How many squares are contained in the shape above? Make sure you consider all of the different sizes and overlapping shapes.

Hint: try using the small square size to the left as a building block to find all the squares (1x1, 2x2, 3x3, etc.).

See if you can find more than 15.

CUBE PUZZLES

In these exercises, you will be given the faces, as well as different views of a cube.
Then you must put the faces into a net that, when folded, makes the cube.

Example:

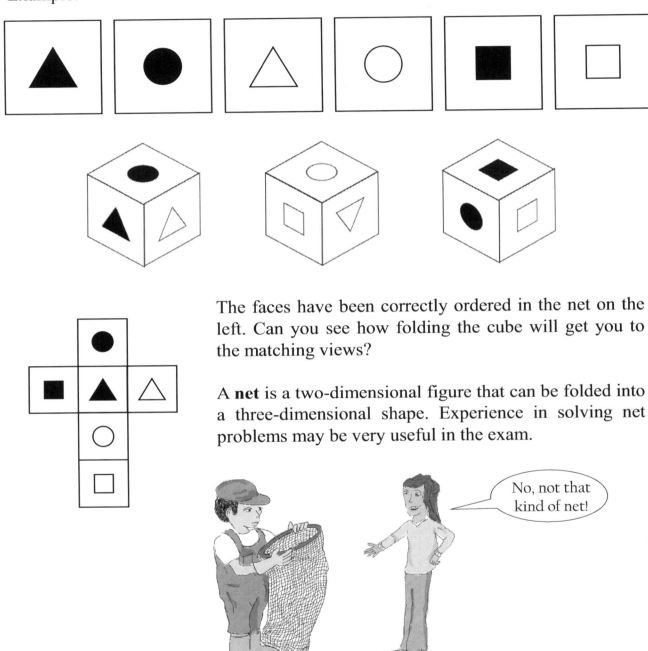

The faces have been correctly ordered in the net on the
left. Can you see how folding the cube will get you to
the matching views?

A **net** is a two-dimensional figure that can be folded into
a three-dimensional shape. Experience in solving net
problems may be very useful in the exam.

No, not that kind of net!

Note that there are eleven possible net designs that can be folded into a cube!

You may also be asked to identify the net that created a cube.

1) Here are the cube faces, given in no particular order:

Here are some views of the cube in different positions.

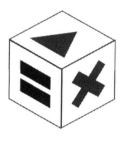 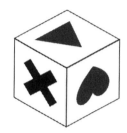 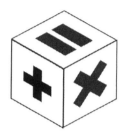

Can you fill out the net that creates this cube?

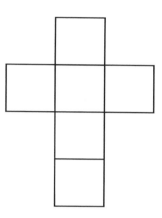

2) Here are the cube faces, given in no particular order:

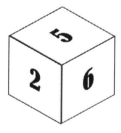 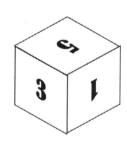 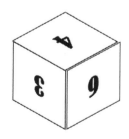

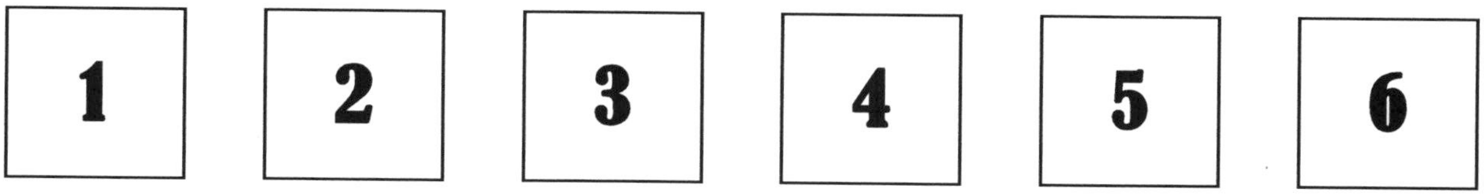

1	2	3	4	5	6

Here are some views of the cube in different positions.

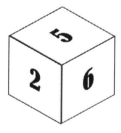 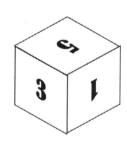 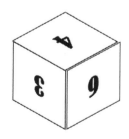

Can you fill out the net that creates this cube?

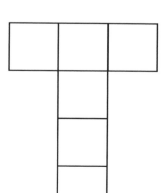

3) Find the net that created this cube:

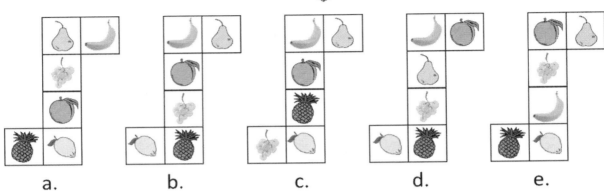

a.　　　b.　　　c.　　　d.　　　e.

4) Find the net that created this cube:

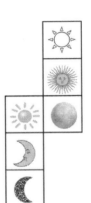

a.　　　b.　　　c.　　　d.

5) Find the net that created this cube:

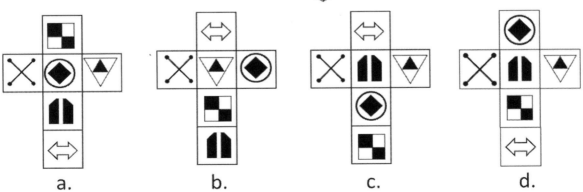

a.　　　b.　　　c.　　　d.

Number Logic Puzzle

(or 'Fill in the Blanks')

Work out which of the numbers go into each space. A few of the answers have already been done.

2-DIGIT NUMBERS	3-DIGIT NUMBERS		4-DIGIT NUMBERS		5-DIGIT NUMBERS	
12	255	501	1043	4231	14793	51104
18	319	795	1999	4768	17320	58931
~~22~~	~~322~~	848	2051	6129	19535	71389
59	365	888	~~2447~~	7312	~~26914~~	75924
63			~~2501~~	7459	34922	81403
82			2927	9111	39971	
			3848		45535	

Triples

The object of this game is to help relate fractions to percentages and decimals. Use the set of Triples cards for this exercise. Cut out and shuffle the cards.

This game is played in a similar way to the traditional game of Pairs. Lay out all of the cards, so the numbers cannot be seen. The first player selects three cards and turns them over, hoping to find three matching values.

If there is no match, the cards must be turned back over. The next player goes and turns over three cards, again hoping to find a triple. If a player finds a triple they get to keep it.

At the end of the game, the player who has the most triples wins.

Converting between fractions, percentages and decimals (examples)
Unless you can remember certain fractions as a percentage, a good way is to convert the fraction's denominator to 100

$$\frac{1}{4} \implies = \frac{25}{100} = 0.25 = 25\%$$

$$0.35 \implies = \frac{35}{100} = 35\% = \frac{7}{20}$$

$$14\% \implies = \frac{14}{100} = 0.14 = \frac{7}{50}$$

For the exam, remember these conversions by heart. They will come in very handy!

$25\% = \frac{1}{4} = 0.25$	$100\% = \frac{1}{1} = 1.0$
$20\% = \frac{1}{5} = 0.20$	$75\% = \frac{3}{4} = 0.75$
$12.5\% = \frac{1}{8} = 0.125$	$50\% = \frac{1}{2} = 0.5$

1%	$\dfrac{1}{100}$	0.01
5%	$\dfrac{1}{20}$	0.05
10%	$\dfrac{1}{10}$	0.10
20%	$\dfrac{1}{5}$	0.20
25%	$\dfrac{1}{4}$	0.25
30%	$\dfrac{3}{10}$	0.30
45%	$\dfrac{9}{20}$	0.45
50%	$\dfrac{1}{2}$	0.50
60%	$\dfrac{3}{5}$	0.60

Triples	**Triples**	**Triples**
Triples	**Triples**	**Triples**
Triples	**Triples**	**Triples**
Triples	**Triples**	**Triples**
Triples	**Triples**	**Triples**
Triples	**Triples**	**Triples**
Triples	**Triples**	**Triples**
Triples	**Triples**	**Triples**
Triples	**Triples**	**Triples**

Act Your Age

Try to see if you can find out the ages based on the clues given. Watch out, some of these can be tricky!

1) Max is three times as old as Martin. The sum of their ages is 44. How old is Max now?

2) My Dad's age this year is a multiple of 8. Next year it will be a multiple of 7. How old is he?

3) My Mum was 33 on my 2nd birthday. How old will she be on my 33rd birthday?

4) Last year Lonnie's age was a square number. Next year, it will be a cube number. How old is Lonnie now?

5) In four years' time, Ali will be twice as old as he was four years ago. How old is he now?

6) Lucy has two dogs. Two years ago, the combined age of the dogs was 12. What will be the combined ages in two years' time?

7) A man is aged 69 years, 14 months, 52 weeks and 4 days. How old will he be on his next birthday?

8) My age is a multiple of 7. Next year it will be a multiple of 5. I am older than 21 but younger than 80. How old am I?

9) Julius is 10 years old and his sister is 21. How old will Julius be when his sister is seven times as old as Julius was 5 years ago?

10) You are given the clues below. Can you figure out who is the youngest?

> Tanya is older than Emily
>
> Olivia is older than Tanya but is younger than Vijay
>
> Jasmin is younger than Tanya
>
> Kyle is older than Olivia
>
> Emily is younger than Jasmin

Divisibility Rules

These are rules you should remember for numbers to be divided evenly – with no remainders (whole numbers):

A number is divisible by	If...	Example
2	The last digit is an even number.	**104** 4 is divisible by 2
3	The sum of the digits is divisible by 3	**513** (5+1+3=9) 9 is divisible by 3
4	The last two digits are a number divisible by 4	**932** 32 is divisible by 4
5	The last digit is either a 5 or 0	**3,925** or **9,230** Both divisible by 5
6	The number is divisible by **both** 2 and 3	**90** 90 is divisible by both 2 and 3
7	You can double the last digit, and then subtract it from the remaining digits – giving an answer divisible by 7	**175** 5+5=10 17 – 10 = 7 7 is divisible by 7
8	The last three digits of the number are divisible by 8	**7,096** 96 is divisible by 8
9	The sum of all the digits is divisible by 9	**954** 9+5+4=18 18 is divisible by 9
10	The number ends in 0	**265,310** Is divisible by 10

DIVIDE & CONQUER

A game for two players. Cut out the cards and place them by Set into two piles. The first player picks a card from Set 1. This will be the **divisibility number** for both players. Then the first player takes a card from both Set 1 and Set 2, and combines the numbers to form a new number. For example:

- Pick a card for the divisibility number – a 4 is chosen. The divisibility number is 4 for the round.

- Player 1 picks 3 and 7. The number can be combined either as 37 or 73. In this case, neither is divisible by 4. No points for Player 1.

- Player 2 goes next and picks a 4 and an 8. The player announces '48' and knows it is divisible by 4. One point for Player 2.

If the number is divisible by the divisibility number, then you score a point. The first player to reach 10 points wins the game.

Card Set 1	Card Set 2
9	1
4	3
3	5
6	7
8	4
7	0

DIVIDE & CONQUER Card Set 1	DIVIDE & CONQUER Card Set 2
DIVIDE & CONQUER Card Set 1	DIVIDE & CONQUER Card Set 2
DIVIDE & CONQUER Card Set 1	DIVIDE & CONQUER Card Set 2
DIVIDE & CONQUER Card Set 1	DIVIDE & CONQUER Card Set 2
DIVIDE & CONQUER Card Set 1	DIVIDE & CONQUER Card Set 2
DIVIDE & CONQUER Card Set 1	DIVIDE & CONQUER Card Set 2

Minesweeper

Minesweeper is a puzzle, where the goal is to locate all of the mines (marked with an X) in a grid of squares. The numbers in the squares these show the total number of mines surrounding that square (left, right, above, below, and diagonally). You must determine which of the **blank** squares have mines by marking them with an **X**. If the box does not have a mine, write in the appropriate number (0,1,2,3). Use the boxes that already have a number to help you find where the mines are. It is recommended to use a pencil.

Example:

	2	1	1
	3		
1	3		
	2	1	1

four mines

solved →

X	2	1	1
1	(3)	X	2
1	3	X	2
X	2	1	1

3 mines are touching the surrounding squares

1.

0		1	
	2		2
		2	
2		2	1

four mines

2.

	2		2
1			
1	2		2
	1	0	

four mines

3.

	2		
		3	2
2	3		1
	2	1	

five mines

4.

ten mines

1	2		1		0	
				0		1
1		4			2	
0						2
			2			
1		2	1			2
	1			3		

super challenge!

SUDOKU

Sudoku is a popular game of logic where you place the numbers 1 through 9 in a grid, so that each column, each row, and each of the nine 3×3 boxes that compose the grid contain all of the digits from 1 to 9.

In this exercise, fill in the tables below. Make sure that you use only one of each of the nine numbers in each of the 3x3 grids. See the example

1	5	9
7	4	8
2	6	3

grid example

1 Level 1. Beginner (18 numbers missing)

In each column all numbers should appear only once

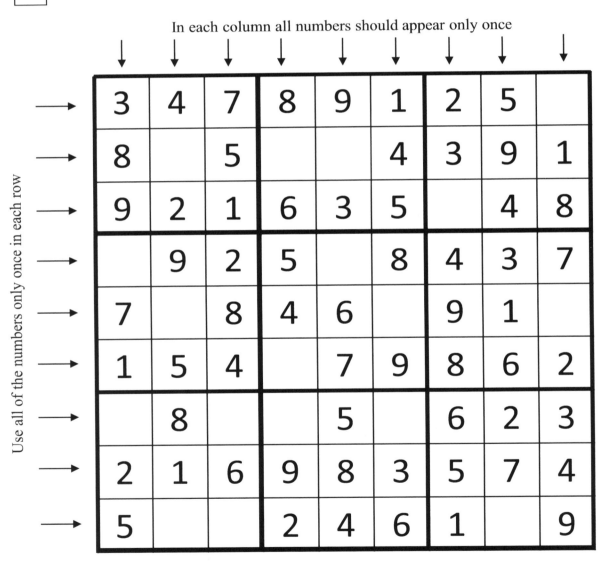

Use all of the numbers only once in each row

3	4	7	8	9	1	2	5	
8		5			4	3	9	1
9	2	1	6	3	5		4	8
	9	2	5		8	4	3	7
7		8	4	6		9	1	
1	5	4		7	9	8	6	2
	8			5		6	2	3
2	1	6	9	8	3	5	7	4
5			2	4	6	1		9

78

2 Level 2. Intermediate (24 numbers missing)

	6		2	5	8	9		4
2	5	1	9	4				3
4		8		7	1	6	2	5
8	3	2	6	1	5		9	7
		6	7		2	3	5	
1		5	4	3		8	6	2
5	8	7	1		3	2	4	
	1			2	4			6
6	2	4	5		7	1		8

3 Level 3. Advanced (34 numbers missing)

5		3		7		9		1
1		8	9	4	3			5
	9		5			3	4	
	3	1		5	9	4		6
2		5		6			7	
	6	9	1		7	5	3	8
8		4		9	5	2		3
					2	8	5	
3		2	7		8		9	4

Symbolic Scales

In these exercises you must determine the relative value of different objects by observing how they balance with each other, and using your mathematical deduction skills.

1

All of the scales shown are balanced

Observe the balanced relationships amongst the octopus, starfish and seahorses.

How many seahorses will be needed to balance the scales?

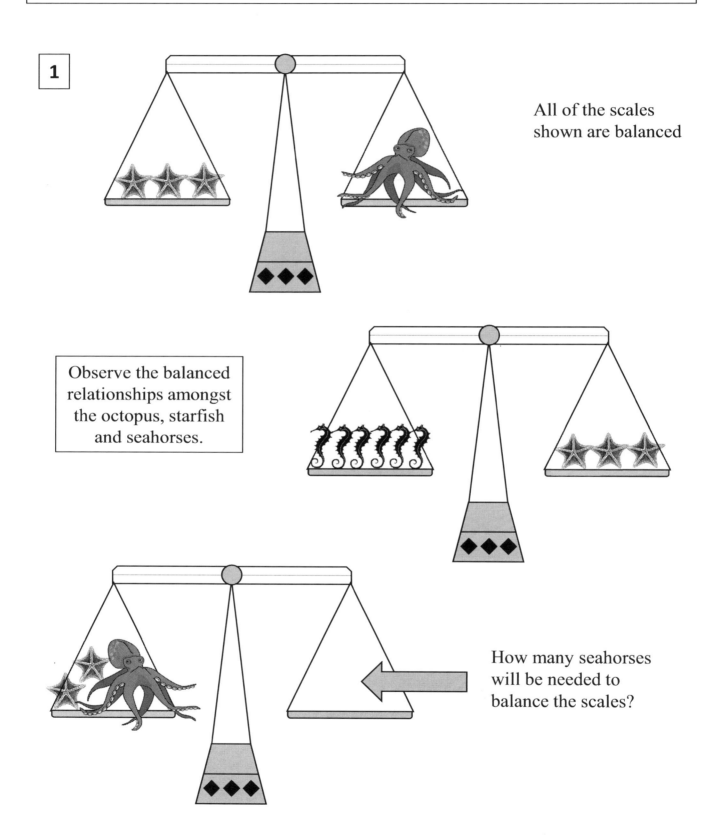

2

All of the scales shown are balanced

Observe the balanced relationships amongst the trilby hats, party hats and caps.

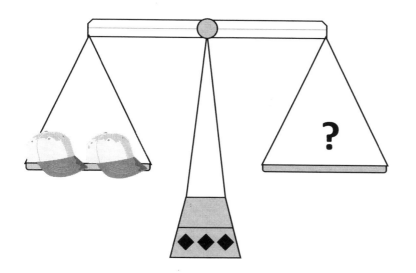

How many trilby hats will be needed to balance the scales?

81

3

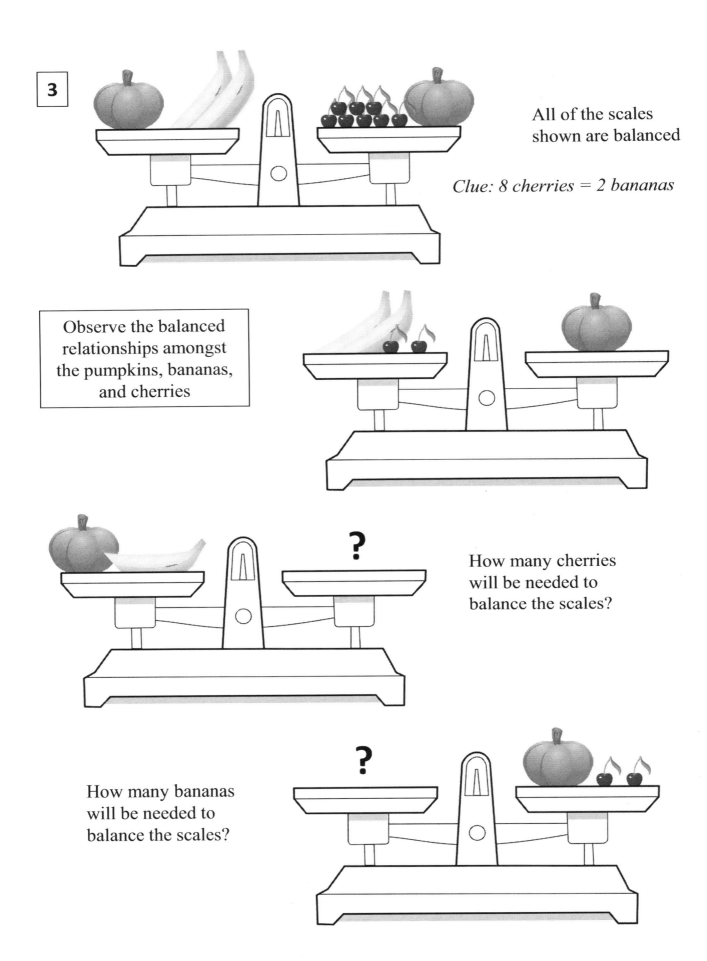

All of the scales shown are balanced

Clue: 8 cherries = 2 bananas

Observe the balanced relationships amongst the pumpkins, bananas, and cherries

How many cherries will be needed to balance the scales?

How many bananas will be needed to balance the scales?

4

All of the scales shown are balanced

Observe the balanced relationships amongst the teddy bears, pandas and elephants

?

How many teddy bears will be needed to balance the scales?

How many pandas will be needed to balance the scales?

?

The Need for Speed Game

In this game, take turns selecting one of the cards. You have to look at both sides and decide which side – A or B – is *faster* (or less time). If you are correct, you keep the card. If you are wrong, the card goes back to the bottom of the pile. You may decide how many of the cards to use. The player who has the most cards at the end of the game is the winner.

The answers to all of the questions can be found in the Answer Key.

As a bonus, see if you can determine which of the cards has the fastest, and the longest time.

Helpful Game Tips

Use these conversions if you need some help:

one minute = 60 seconds

one hour = 3,600 seconds

one day = 86,400 seconds

one week = 604,800 seconds

30 days = 2,592,000 Seconds

24 hours = one day

168 hours = one week

720 hours = 30 days

8,766 hours = 365 days = one year

60 minutes = one hour

1,440 minutes = one day

10,080 minutes = one week

43,200 minutes = 30 days

A year has 365 days

A leap year has an extra day

1. Side A 7 hours, 23 minutes	**2. Side A** 3 days, 4 hours
3. Side A The months of July, August, and September	**4. Side A** 703 hours, and 2 days
5. Side A ten days, and one second	**6. Side A** 2,000 minutes
7. Side A 3 hours, and 20 minutes	**8. Side A** February (in a Leap Year), January, May, and September
9. Side A 90 miles at 45 miles per hour	**10. Side A** 09:32 to 17:51
11. Side A 720 hours	**12. Side A** Two decades

2. Side B 75 hours	**1. Side B** 500 minutes
4. Side B 30 days	**3. Side B** 101 days
6. Side B 2 days	**5. Side B** 864,100 seconds
8. Side B 120 days	**7. Side B** 199 minutes
10. Side B 8 hours, 4 minutes	**9. Side B** 130 minutes
12. Side B 12 years	**11. Side B** The month of May

A Tangle of Rectangles

How many rectangles are contained in the shape above? Make sure you consider all of the different sizes and overlapping shapes.

You may want to number each individual rectangle.

Maths Vocabulary Word Search

Let's check some of the important Maths terms and then find them in the word search puzzle on the next page.

Definition	**Answer**
1) The flat part of a solid 3D shape	_____
2) A triangle whose sides have different lengths	_____
3) The average value of a set of numbers	_____
4) Two lines that join at the same vertex	_____
5) The midpoint of a set of numbers arranged by size	_____
6) The surface of a 2D shape measured in square units	_____
7) Two lines that never meet, and have the same continuous distance between them	_____
8) The distance around something	_____
9) An angle that is less than 90°	_____
10) Having the same size and shape	_____
11) A triangle having 2 equal sides and 2 equal angles	_____
12) A comparison of two numbers or quantities	_____
13) A solid 3D shape with parallel sides and two flat, circular faces	_____
14) The length of a straight line from the centre of a circle to the circumference	_____
15) A number greater than 1, whose only factors are 1 and itself	_____
16) One of a pair of numbers used to locate a point	_____
17) The number above the line in a fraction	_____
18) A two-dimensional shape formed with straight lines	_____
19) One hundred years	_____
20) A number that is not a fraction, a whole number	_____

WORD BANK

acute	adjacent	area	century	circumference
congruent	coordinate	cylinder	face	integer
isosceles	median	mean	numerator	parallel
polygon	prime	radius	ratio	scalene

Find these words in the puzzle below. Words can be forwards or backwards in the puzzle vertically, horizontally or diagonally.

acute   adjacent   area   century   circumference

congruent   coordinate   cylinder   face   integer

isosceles   median   mean   numerator   parallel

polygon   prime   radius   ratio   scalene

A	S	A	Y	C	E	C	N	E	R	E	F	M	U	C	R	I	C
O	C	P	R	I	M	E	T	D	O	L	C	E	G	O	P	G	R
T	A	U	U	Y	A	W	O	L	U	O	D	A	S	O	B	U	C
W	L	L	T	H	D	I	N	T	E	G	E	R	J	R	S	Y	O
Y	E	A	N	E	J	S	M	W	G	R	A	P	B	D	L	M	L
R	I	Y	E	A	N	O	O	R	A	D	I	S	D	I	A	G	R
T	L	D	C	O	I	S	B	A	I	O	U	R	N	N	H	E	Q
S	I	Y	D	T	Z	C	I	U	N	Y	N	D	L	A	S	Y	N
C	W	P	A	N	M	E	S	Q	M	I	E	C	P	T	O	L	T
A	Y	R	S	B	G	L	O	K	N	R	F	A	C	E	B	I	N
L	H	O	U	W	L	E	E	M	O	C	D	Z	Y	U	R	A	E
E	N	T	S	I	G	S	L	I	G	E	F	K	W	G	I	S	C
N	I	A	G	H	W	M	L	B	Y	O	R	O	M	D	B	E	A
E	O	R	X	P	A	R	A	L	L	E	L	N	E	S	M	T	J
G	E	E	Q	G	L	E	N	S	O	R	W	M	A	U	E	A	D
N	U	M	B	E	R	Y	R	T	P	E	A	R	N	R	A	R	A
O	A	U	O	V	W	J	V	A	Q	O	U	P	A	E	S	E	U
C	O	N	G	R	U	E	N	T	C	A	R	A	E	R	R	M	Y

Maths Crossword

Solve like you would for a regular crossword

Across

1) 7^2

4) $2000 - 665$

7) $6,000 - 2,744$

8) The 4th Triangular number x 2

9) $28b + 5$ (where $b = 5$)

11) The mean of these numbers:

     54   31   12   100   23

13) 4^2

15) CCLXIV

16) Volume of a cube with sides '3' long

18) The 7th prime number minus the 4th prime number

19) 5 million $- 799,703$

21) $1,238 \times 2$

24) If the radius of a circle is 50½ cm, what is its diameter?

27) The number of lines of symmetry of a hexagon, x 7

28) $\frac{3}{5} \times 125$

29) The area of a triangle with a base of 120 and a height of 7

30) $\frac{2}{4} \times 125,428$

Down

2) The range of these numbers:

302   415   1,296   522   1,000

3) $12^2 - 20$

4) $\frac{2}{7}$ of 56

5) 8×4

6) $8^2 - 14$

10) 128×4

12) 0.002222×1 million

14) $\frac{3}{4}$ of 800 $+ 74$

17) The diameter of a circle with a radius of 30

18) $11^2 + 11$

20) The number of sides of a nonagon x $10 + 4$

22) The volume of a cuboid with sides measuring 2, 2, and 11

23) Solve for this sequence:

    32   62   39   67   46   ___

24) The perimeter of a parallelogram with sides 60 and 18.5 cm long

25) $(6 + 6)^2$

26) $\frac{2}{3}$ of 912

28) $3^2 \times 8$

Maths Crossword

'no words just numbers!'

Magic Squares

Magic Squares are interesting puzzles, which are made using a set of consecutive numbers. In order to be 'magic,' all of the rows and columns, as well as diagonals, add up to the same number.

In this example, the **magic number** is **15** in this order 3 puzzle (3 rows, 3 columns).

Note also in the puzzle, that the two numbers opposite the centre number, add up to the same number (10).

Note that the **magic number** changes based on the numbers in the grid.

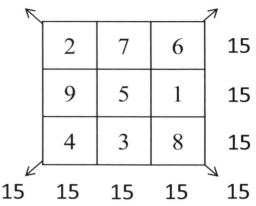

Can you fill out the magic squares below? You are given the magic number, which means all of the rows, columns, and diagonals must add up to that number. *Hint: all of these examples are using consecutive numbers, so first try to work out what numbers are missing.*

8		4
	5	
6		2

a. The magic number is 15
Numbers start with 1

16	9	
		15
12	17	

b. The magic number is 39
Numbers start with 9

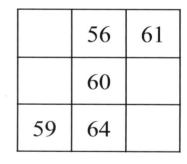

c. The magic number is 180
Numbers start with 56

	6	
8		12
	14	

d. The magic number is 30
Numbers start with 6

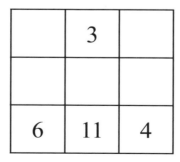

e. The magic number is 21
Numbers start with 3

18		16
	15	17
	19	

f. The magic number is 45
Numbers start with 11

Magic Squares

Magic Squares can even get larger! Try these if you are up to the challenge!

18		5	15
	13	12	10
11	9	8	
6			3

g. The magic number for this order 4 puzzle (4 rows, 4 columns) is 42

The consecutive numbers start with 3 and end with 18

15		-1	6	13
	3	5		14
2	4	11	18	20
	10	17	19	
9		23		7

h. The magic number for this order 5 puzzle is 55

Note that the consecutive numbers start with -1, and don't forget 0!

35	26		19	6	24
8		28	10	33	
3	21	32		7	25
		5	14	34	16
31	22		27	2	20
4	13	36		29	

i. The magic number for this order 6 puzzle is 111

The consecutive numbers start with 1

What Can You See?

In these exercises we will look from the point of view of some animals or other things, and try to determine how many there are in total.

<u>Example</u>: There are a number of horses and pigs in a field. Each horse can see one more pig than horse. Each pig can also see one more horse than it can see pigs. A pig can see three pigs and four horses. How many pigs and horses are there?

Answer: There are equal numbers of horses and pigs. Each animal sees one extra of the other, because it was not counting itself. Since we were told that one pig could see four horses, there must be four pigs.

Keep in mind the point of view in these questions – that the one seeing and counting is <u>not</u> including itself.

1) Some aliens from a remote galaxy have landed in a cow field in Wiltshire. Each alien can see twice as many cows as aliens. Each cow can see the same number of aliens as cows. How many aliens and cows are there?

2) Some cats decide to go into a barn for the night. Upon entering the barn, they notice that there are some owls already nesting there. Each cat can see three times as many owls as cats. Each owl can see the same number of cats as owls. How many cats and owls are there?

3) A fish tank has a number of guppies and mollies. Each guppy can see twice as many mollies as guppies; each molly can see two more mollies than guppies. How many guppies and how many mollies are in the tank?

4) Some school children go into a hall and are surprised to see there are robots conducting a lesson. Each child can see twice as many robots as children. Each of the robots can see one more robot than child. How many children and robots are there?

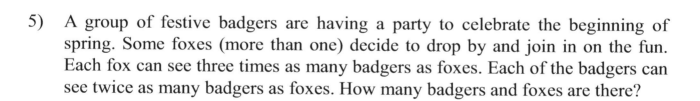

5) A group of festive badgers are having a party to celebrate the beginning of spring. Some foxes (more than one) decide to drop by and join in on the fun. Each fox can see three times as many badgers as foxes. Each of the badgers can see twice as many badgers as foxes. How many badgers and foxes are there?

SHOW ME THE MONEY

Worded maths problems can be tricky because it can be hard to decide which operations to use, and in what order.

Example: Grace had an amount of money (N). She divided it equally among herself and her two friends. They went to the cinema and spent £9 each. The total that each girl now had remaining was £12. How much money did Grace have at the beginning?

If you write this as an expression for how much each girl has, it would look like this:

$$\frac{N}{3} - 9 = 12$$

The original amount (N) was divided by three (Grace and 2 friends), then we subtract the 9 pounds they spent at the cinema, giving us 12 pounds remaining.

Solving for N, the answer is £63

Now try to solve these questions about money.

1) Brian's parents are going on holiday in Spain for the summer. They will be staying at a villa that costs 200 Euros per day, plus a 75 Euro cleaning charge when they leave. If they stay for exactly three weeks, how much will it cost to stay at the villa?

    a.   2875 Euros

    b.   4200 Euros

    c.   4275 Euros

    d.   6075 Euros

2) The cost of an omelette at a restaurant is 3 pounds, plus 50p for each egg (e) used to make the omelette. Which expression would you use to show the total cost?

   a. $3 + 0.05e$

   b. $3e + 0.50e$

   c. $3 + 5e$

   d. $3 + \frac{1}{2}e$

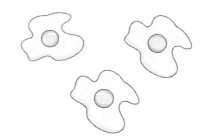

3) Mary needs to hire some equipment for her job as a DJ. There is a fixed charge of £25, and it costs an additional £14 per week. If she spent £193 in total, how many weeks did she have the equipment?

4) Jemima has a recipe for spaghetti that uses 2kg of mince to serve 8 people. However, she is having only 6 people over for dinner, including herself. How much mince should she buy?

Getting harder

5) Mrs. Wilson left half of her money to her son Wilf, and half of that amount to her daughter Rachel. She left 20% to her cousin, and the remaining amount, £50,000, was given to various charities.

   How much money did Mrs. Wilson leave in total?

6) Finlay and Nicole had £50 between them and decided to go out to a restaurant for a fantastic Italian meal. Then took a taxi home. The taxi cost half of the cost of the meal, and all they had left at the end of the evening was £2.

   How much did they spend on dinner?

   How much did the taxi cost?

IMAGINARY MATHS HISTORY

Sir Cumference
Circled the globe

Priscilla Perpen Dicular
Founder of the 90° Society

Henry the ⅛
King and Inventor of the pizza wheel

O. B. Long
singer/songwriter of the
worldwide #1 hit, *I'm not a square*

The Numerator
Sent back in time to save a
fraction of the world

Weighty Matters

In this game, you will test your knowledge of metric units of weight, length, and volume, as well as conversion of some imperial unit measures. These tables will be useful:

Weight
1 gram (g) = 1000 milligrams (mg)
100 grams (g) = 0.1 kilograms (kg)
1000 grams (g) = 1 kilogram (kg)
1000 kilograms (kg) = 1 tonne

Volume
0.1 litres (l) = 100 millilitres (ml)
1 litre (l) = 100 centilitres (cl)
1 litre (l) = 1,000 millilitres (ml)

Length
1 centimetre (cm) = 10 millimetres (mm)
1 metre (m) = 100 centimetres (cm)
1 kilometre (km) = 1,000 metres (m)

For the old imperial units, it is handy to have a good idea of the metric equivalent.

**1 pint = 568 ml
(or 0.568 l)**

**1 inch = 2.5 cm
(or 25mm)**

1 foot = 12 inches = 30 cm

1 mile = 1.6 km

Cut out the cards on the next two pages. Shuffle them and put in a pile with the 'Weighty Matters' side facing up. Players will take turns answering the questions on the back of the card. If the player answers correctly, then they should fill in a piece of the pie chart below.

Note that the sections are divided into weight, length, capacity and imperial. To win, you must be the first to correctly answer a question in each category correctly. You must draw the cards in order after they have been shuffled. If you get a Length card, for example, and you already have a correct answer, you must not skip it but answer correctly, otherwise you will lose a turn. You may want to use a pencil and paper to figure out some of the questions.

There are 24 cards, with 6 cards in each category. You can find the answers in the back.

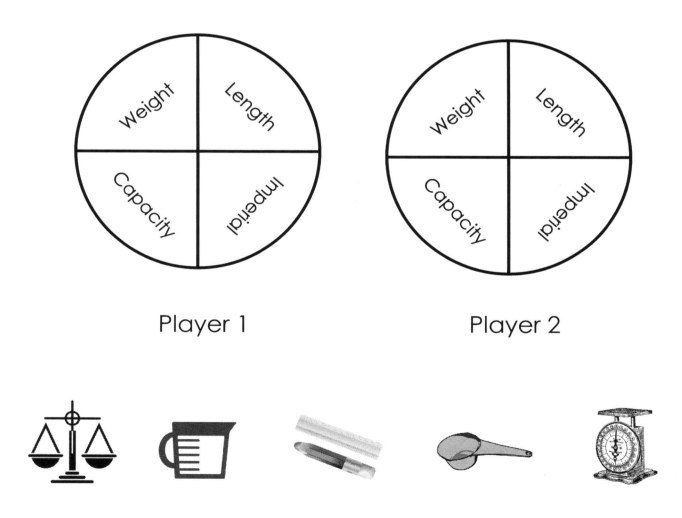

Player 1   Player 2

Weighty Matters	**Weighty Matters**
Weighty Matters	**Weighty Matters**
Weighty Matters	**Weighty Matters**
Weighty Matters	**Weighty Matters**
Weighty Matters	**Weighty Matters**
Weighty Matters	**Weighty Matters**

Length	Length
What is longer?	What is longer?
a. 6 kilometres b. 60,000 centimetres	a. 1200 metres b.12,000 centimetres

Length	Length
What is longer?	What is shorter?
a. 1000 millimetres	a. 2.5 centimetres
b. 10 metres	b. 0.0025 kilometres

Length	Length
What is shorter?	What is shorter?
a. 39 centimetres b. 3900 millimetres	a. 12,676 metres
	b. 1.2676 kilometres

Weight	Weight
What is heavier?	What is heavier?
a. 1000 kilograms b. 10 tonnes	a. 100,000 milligrams
	b. 1 kilogram

Weight	Weight
What is heavier?	What weighs less?
a. 60 milligrams b. 0.6 grams	a. 1 tonne b. 10,000,000 grams

Weight	Weight
What weighs less?	What weighs less?
a. 99 milligrams b. 0.99 grams	a. 5 grams
	b. 55,000 milligrams

Weighty Matters

Weighty Matters

Weighty Matters

Weighty Matters

Weighty Matters

Weighty Matters

Weighty Matters

Weighty Matters

Weighty Matters

Weighty Matters

Weighty Matters

Weighty Matters

Volume Which is more? a. 100 milliltres b. 1 litre	**Volume** Which is more? a. 5,250 millilitres b. 5 litres
Volume Which is more? a. 70,000 millilitres b. 8 litres	**Volume** Which is less? a. 1.201 litres b. 1200 millilitres
Volume Which is less? a. 7.1 litres b. 7,400 millilitres	**Volume** Which is less? a. 49 litres b. 4,990 millilitres
Imperial What is longer? a. 500 miles b. 500 km	**Imperial** What is shorter? a. 25 inches b. 25 cm
Imperial Which is more? a. One litre b. Two pints	**Imperial** What is longer? a. 2 metres b. 5 feet
Imperial What is less? a. One pint b. 500 ml	**Imperial** Which is shorter? a. 10 miles b. 20 km

FROM A DIFFERENT ANGLE

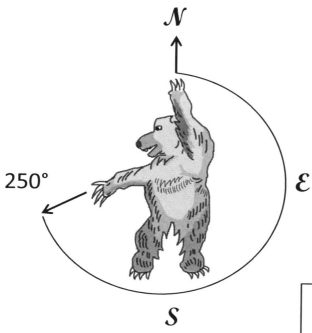

250°

Bears never get lost because they tend to keep their **bearings**. (Always measured clockwise from the North, of course)

The bicycle-riding insect crossed the line, dividing it into two parts (**bisect**)

You'll be staying in Room (15,5). It's just along the corridor and up the stairs

James liked to stay at the **Coordinates** Hotel.

(15,5)

(0,0)

y-axis

x-axis

The 180° Game

This game will help you remember regular polygons and angles. As you add a new side to each shape, this adds 180 degrees (a new triangle) to the total sum of the angles.

Cut out the shape cards and stack into a pile.

Player 1 must correctly guess the name of the first polygon they pick, with the number of sides, and the total sum of the angles inside the shape. If the player incorrectly guesses, then player 2 can win the card by guessing the correct answers.

Continue playing until all of the cards have been won. The player with the most cards wins.

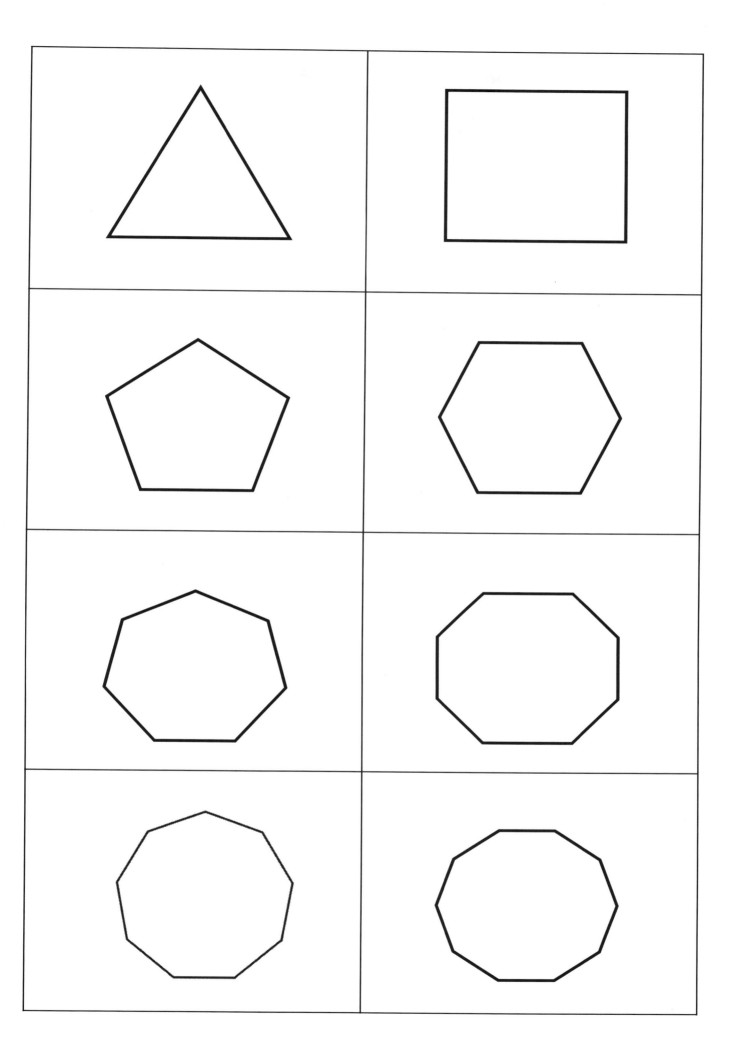

Square 4 sides **360°**	Triangle 3 sides **180°**
Hexagon 6 sides **720°**	Pentagon 5 sides **540°**
Octagon 8 sides **1080°**	Heptagon 7 sides **900°**
Decagon 10 sides **1440°**	Nonagon 9 sides **1260°**

The Nth Term

These questions may be new to you, but they are not too tricky once you know a simple rule.

The nth term can be described as the position of a number in a sequence.

Example: Using the expression $4n - 2$. The following numbers fit

Positions of the number >	**1**	**2**	**3**	**4**	**5**	**6**	**7**	**8**
Expression answer >	2	6	10	14	18	22	26	30

You may be asked to find the 5th term using the expression $3n + 10$. In this case, $3n = 3 \times 5$ (the 5th term) $= 15 + 10 = 25$

Try these: Find the 5th term in these sequences:

The expression is $6n \div 3$ (answer: $6 \times 5 = 30$, $30 \div 3 = 10$)

The expression is $4n - 6$ (answer: $4 \times 5 = 20$, $20 - 6 = 14$)

The expression is $5 + 12n$ (answer: $12 \times 5 = 60$, $60 + 5 = 65$)

The expression is $3n \times 3$ (answer: $3 \times 5 = 15$, $15 \times 3 = 45$)

You may also be asked to provide the expression, or the sequence.

Example: What is the expression for the sequence: -1, 2, 5, 8, 11, 14

a) $n - 2$ b) $n + 2$ c) $3n - 4$ d) $2n - 3$

In this case, comparing the possible answers by trial and error will lead you to the correct answer. **The answer is c) $3n - 4$**

Example: Which is the correct sequence for this expression? $3n + 5$

a) 8, 11, 14, 17   b) 8, 12, 16, 24   c) -4, 8, 16, 18   d) 9, 12, 14, 18

The answer is **a) 8, 11, 14, 17**

The Nth Term Game

In this game, you will use the formula cards, and the number position cards on the following pages. After cutting them out, shuffle and put them in separate piles.

The first player will pick up one of each cards. The player should use the number position card as the nth term in the formula and find the answer. Then mark their initials in the box with the answer on the grid below. The second player goes next and does the same.

If a player comes up with an answer that has already been used, then the player gets no score for that turn.

The player to correctly mark off 10 answers first is the winner. The answers to the formulas are in the Answer Key.

1	2	3	4	5	6	7	8	9	10
11	12	13	14	15	16	17	18	19	20
21	22	23	24	25	26	27	28	29	30
31	32	33	34	35	36	37	38	39	40
41	42	43	44	45	46	47	48	49	50
51	52	53	54	55	56	57	58	59	60
61	62	63	64	65	66	67	68	69	70
71	72	73	74	75	76	77	78	79	80
81	82	83	84	85	86	87	88	89	90
91	92	93	94	95	96	97	98	99	100

Answer Grid

$2n + 7$	$5n + 2$
$3n - 2$	$10n - 5$
$n + 24$	$9n/3$
$8n/4$	$6n + 3$
$7n - 3$	$4n - 3$
$3n \times 3$	$2n \times 5$

FORMULA CARDS

Formula Card	Formula Card
Formula Card	Formula Card
Formula Card	Formula Card
Formula Card	Formula Card
Formula Card	Formula Card
Formula Card	Formula Card

1	1	1	1
2	2	2	2
3	3	3	3
4	4	4	4
5	5	5	5
6	6	6	6
7	7	7	7
8	8	8	8
9	9	9	9
10	10	10	10

NUMBER POSITION CARDS

Number position card	Number position card	Number position card	Number position card
Number position card	Number position card	Number position card	Number position card
Number position card	Number position card	Number position card	Number position card
Number position card	Number position card	Number position card	Number position card
Number position card	Number position card	Number position card	Number position card
Number position card	Number position card	Number position card	Number position card
Number position card	Number position card	Number position card	Number position card
Number position card	Number position card	Number position card	Number position card
Number position card	Number position card	Number position card	Number position card
Number position card	Number position card	Number position card	Number position card

IN ANOTHER DIMENSION

Locked in a Triangular Prism

Trapped by a Trapezium

The extremes people go to make polygon puns

Transformation mis-translation

Number Analogies

The Eleven Plus is all about spotting patterns. Let's see how well you can do this. In this game, look the numbers on the left. Try to determine the pattern (or analogy) that best fits from the selections on the right. The first problem has been done as an example.

1) 13   is to   16,   as   16   is to:    7   25   8   0

The answer is <u>19</u>, the pattern is to add 3 (3 greater)

2) 4 is to 16,   as 7 is to: 4   45   81   49   27

3) 95 is to 19,   as 60 is to: 20   65   12   7   18

4) 19 is to 4,   as 31 is to: 16   24   15   6   14

5) triangle is to 180, as hexagon is to: 540   360   720   180   90

6) 3t is to 18,   as 6t is to: 24   36   40   19   7

7) $\frac{3}{5}$ is to 60%, as $\frac{6}{8}$ is to: 80%   75%   45%   20%   60%

8) 0.091 is to 910, as   0.83 is to: 830   8300   0.830   8.300

9) 40% is to 200, as   20% is to: 10,000   200   10   200   100

Number Analogies

10) $7\frac{5}{8}$ is to $\frac{61}{8}$ as 9 is to: $7\frac{2}{5}$ $\frac{45}{5}$ $8\frac{3}{5}$ $\frac{81}{8}$ $\frac{18}{3}$

11) 7:25 is to 21:15, as 3:04 is to: 14:00   16:54   14:20   17:04

12) 31 is to March, as 30 is to: Dec   Nov   Jan   Feb   Jul

13) $\frac{1}{8}$ is to 12.5%, as $\frac{4}{5}$ is to: 75%   80%   15%   90%   60%

14) 7 is to 84, as 13 is to: 125   25   100   96   156

15) 3 is to 27, as 5 is to: 52   125   150   75   64

16) $\frac{1}{2}$ is to 100%, as $\frac{1}{5}$ is to: 25%   80%   66%   40%   30%

17) 12 is to 144, as 9 is to: 27   36   90   81   118

18) 6 is to 9, as 12 is to : 14   18   21   24   48

19) 23:00 is to 11:00, as 18:00 is to: 05:00   07:00   06:00   10:00

20) 0.75 is to $\frac{3}{4}$ as 0.80 is to: $\frac{13}{14}$ $\frac{10}{8}$ $\frac{12}{15}$ $\frac{3}{4}$ $\frac{10}{15}$

Squares / Noughts & Crosses

This section uses 13 sets of 25 review questions each to play the games of Squares, or Noughts & Crosses. The questions are organised by Maths topics. This will give you a chance to review these areas whilst playing a fun game. Remember, players must answer a question correctly before they make a mark! The answers to the questions can be found in the Answer Key.

Squares – Game Rules

In this game, use the dotted grid to make as many squares as possible. Players take turns by answering review questions. If they give a correct answer, then they can connect two of the dots.

If a player can complete a square, then they put their initial in that square. We have provided grids with 16 possible squares, so the first player to reach 9 squares will win a game.

You can also make your own smaller or larger grids.

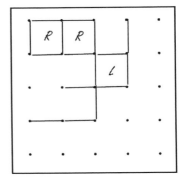

Noughts and Crosses – Game Rules

Similar to our book *The Big 11+ Vocabulary Play Book*, the game of noughts and crosses can be played either in the traditional 9 square singular game, or the 'extreme' version which uses 9 separate grids at the same time.

The second version (extreme) demands a great deal of strategic thinking.. This form uses the whole sheet of nine games. As in the traditional way, players take turns by answering one of the review questions. Players can mark their X or O in any square on the sheet. In effect, you are playing nine games at once! The player who can win three individual grids horizontally, vertically, or diagonally wins the game (See example below).

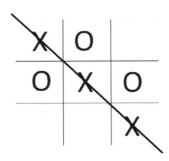

Crosses player winning
Regular version

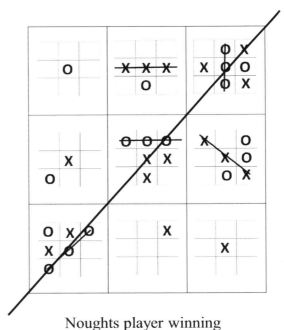

Noughts player winning
Extreme version

Squares

Game Grids

Squares

Game Grids

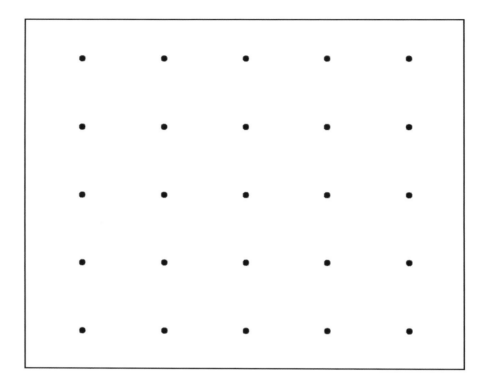

Squares

Game Grids

Noughts & Crosses

Game Grids

Noughts & Crosses

Game Grids

Noughts & Crosses

Game Grids

Four Operations

1) 36 cinema tickets cost £1,008. How much is one ticket?

2) 11.072 + 3.59

3) 4003 + 48

4) 475 x 0.37

5) 10,000 – 99

6) 630,000 ml of water is separated into 30 tanks. How many litres are there in each tank?

7) 3007 – 0.04

8) 42 – 79

9) 64 x 50

10) 0.42 x 5

11) A number is divided by 12 and then multiplied by 15. The answer is 7,200. What was the original number?

12) 4kg + 75g

13) – 4 – 8

14) 3.06 x 1000

15) 273,005 x 100

16) A carton holds 6 jars of jam. 4 cartons were sent to a shop to be sold. If all of the jam sold for £108, then how much was each jar?

17) 6.4 – ? = 0.6

18) – 8 + 16

19) 7.1 x 7

20) 4.98 + 19.97

21) A ribbon of 2.4 m is cut into six equal parts. How much is the length (in metres) of 4 pieces of ribbon?

22) 24.1 – 5.07

23) If 3.76 x 25 = 94   What is 376 x 0.0025?

24) If 222 x 7 = 1,554   What is 222 x 14?

25) Maggie creates bunting with 150 different coloured flags. If 54 are blue, 23 are yellow, 17 are green, 5 are red, 21 are pink, and 18 are orange, then how many are none of these colours?

Algebra

Note: Diagrams are not to scale

1) When $p = 7$ What is $9p$?

2) If $m = 2.5$ and $b = 4.5$ Solve $4m - b$

3) What is the simplified expression for the perimeter of this shape

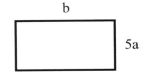

4) James had some money. He gave $\frac{1}{5}$ to his daughter. His daughter received £15. How much did James originally have?

5) $5 \times 9 < 4y$ What is the smallest whole number that y could be?

6) When $21 - 3t = 12$ What is t?

7) How much is d when $30 + 15 = 3d$?

8) What is the simplified expression for the perimeter of this shape?

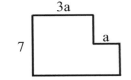

9) What is the value of m? $m - 1\frac{6}{8} = 2\frac{1}{4}$

10) Pat is taking his 3 children to the theatre. Tickets cost t for an adult and 2s for the first child, and k for each of the other children. What is the expression in its simplest form for the total cost of all the tickets?

11) When $3y + 5 = 20$ Then $y = ?$

12) $2b = 6$ What is b?

13) Express the perimeter of the figure on the right in its simplest form.

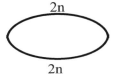

14) Jack says that $3(2a + b)$ is the same as $6a + 6b$. Is he correct?

15) The perimeter of the shape to the right is 48.   How much is n?

16) If $3j = 48$ How much is j?

17) What is the perimeter of this equilateral triangle when $t = 6$?

18) The cost of a haircut is £12 + £6.50 per hour (h) spent. What is the cost of a haircut if 3 hours were spent?

19) If $z = 7$ What is $6(z + 5)$?

20) It takes Rita 96 minutes, including two rest breaks (R), to drive to London. Which below expresses the total time to drive to London without any breaks?

$96 - 2R$ $R + 96 \times 2$ $2R - 96$ $96 + 2R$

21) What is n when $3n + 5 = 26$?

22) Find the value of x when $x \div 4 - 3 = 1$

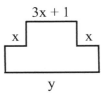

23) Referring to the figure on the right, what is the length of y when $x = 7$?

24) If $k = 9$ what is $2k - 2(k + 0)$?

25) What is the area of the shape to the right? Express in the simplest terms.

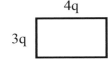

Angles and Direction

1)   What is a complementary angle?

2)   What letter reminds us of alternate angles?

3)   What is the missing angle?

4)   How many degrees are there between S and NE in a clockwise rotation?

5)   From which direction should a bearing always be measured?

6)   What is a reflex angle?

7)   Are opposite angles equal, or different?

8)   What is the missing angle?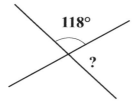

9)   Which direction lies exactly between NNE and SSE?

10)   Are bearings measured in a clockwise or anticlockwise direction?

11)   What is an obtuse angle?

12)   If one angle of an isosceles triangle is 35°, and the other two angles are the same, what is the sum of the other two angles?

13)   What is the missing angle?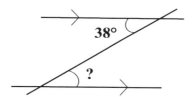

14)   If angles p & q are opposite and the sum of all other angles is 200°, what is the value of both p and q?

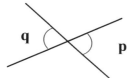

15)   How many degrees are in the angle between NW and E?

16)   What is the sum of the angles of a square?

17)   A triangle with a right angle has another angle of 52°. What is the size of the third angle?

Angles and Direction

18) Three angles of a pentagon are 54°, 47° and 102°. What is the sum of the other angles?

19) What is the missing angle?

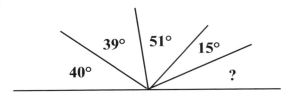

20) What is the bearing from N to K?

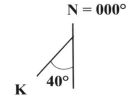

21) What is the sum of the angles of a hexagon?

22) What is the missing angle?

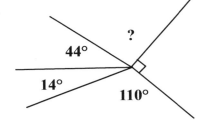

23) If two lines from the same point have an acute angle of 60°, what is their reflex angle size?

24) What is the size of P in this regular rhombus?

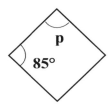

25) Cameron is facing south and turns 225° in an anticlockwise direction. Which direction does he now face?

Probability

1) On the roll of one six-sided dice, what is the probability of scoring less than 4?

2) From the letters P R O B A B I L I T Y, what is the probability of picking a vowel?

3) Dad buys some new pairs of shoes. Three shoes go missing. What is the probability that these are all left-foot shoes?

4) What is the chance of a given year being a leap year?

5) Once a king has been removed from a pack of 52 playing cards, what is the probability that the next card picked would be a king?

6) From the numbers 1 – 13, what is the probability of picking at random a prime number?

7) A bag contains 8 red presents and 14 green presents. There are 24 total presents in the sack. What is the probability of someone taking out a present that is not red or green?

8) What is the probability of someone being born on Christmas Day? (If it is not a leap year)

9) From a deck of 52 playing cards, all of the face cards (jack, queen, king) have been removed. Now what is the probability of selecting an ace?

10) How many ways can you roll a 12 using two six-sided dice?

11) Suzie has a six-sided die and a 10p coin. What is the probability that she will roll a number lower than 5 and get a heads on the flip of the coin?

12) Florence plants six red tulips and nine white tulips. What is the probability that a red tulip will bloom first?

13) In her pencil case Michelle has 12 pencils. 5 are black, 2 are blue, 4 are red and 1 is purple. What is the probability, when she takes a pencil out, that it is red or blue?

14) The chances of Tim winning a game are $^1/_5$. What are his chances of winning two consecutive games?

15) One card is selected at random from a pack of 52 playing cards. What is the probability that it will be a queen? Simplify your answer.

16) Jim has three 10p coins which he tosses. What is the probability that he will get heads on all of them?

17) The chances of it raining tomorrow are 80%. What is this probability expressed as a fraction?

18) Ben tosses two coins – a 50p and a 5p. What is the probability he will get heads on both coins?

19) What is the probability of scoring an even number on a ten-sided die?

20) What is the probability that it will be a weekend day tomorrow or you win a game of football, when there is a 50% chance of winning?

21) With one roll of a six-sided die, what is the probability of rolling a prime number?

22) From the word PANTOMINE, what is the chance of picking a letter that is a vowel?

23) Rose has a 50% chance of going to a party this weekend and a 10% chance of getting money from her grandmother. What is the probability of both happening, expressed as a fraction?

24) What is the probability of rolling an even number on a single roll of a dice?

25) Charlotte read a book with 60 pages. Pages 4, 9, 21, 46, 49 and 60 had pictures. If she opens the book to a random page, what is the probability that it does not have a picture? Simplify your answer.

Percentages

1) Freddie's dad gave him £50. He decided to spend 20% of it on a cinema ticket. How much did he have left?

2) What is $\frac{3}{8}$ expressed as a percentage?

3) In a sale, some shoes have been discounted by 20%. If the original price was £40, how much are they now?

4) Express $^{45}/_{150}$ as a percentage.

5) Mum had to pay an extra tax on a new car. The car cost £20,000 and the tax was an extra 5%. How much did the car cost in total?

6) 0.195 = how much as a percentage?

7) What is $\frac{1}{4}$ of $\frac{1}{2}$ as a percentage?

8) If 68.7% of the population of a city of 1,000,000 own a mobile phone, what percentage do not?

9) Abigail ate $\frac{2}{5}$ of a bag of sweets in the morning and $\frac{2}{25}$ in the afternoon. How much does she have left as a percentage?

10) What is 10% of 60% ? (Hint: change these to decimals and then multiply)

11) If there are 30 children in a class and 12 are girls, what percentage of the class are boys?

12) What is 40% of 18?

13) Robert spent 64% of his £60 allowance on some games. How much does he have left?

14) The price of a tablet costing £400 is reduced by 15%. What does the tablet cost now?

15) Jess bought a coat originally priced at £50. It was reduced by 10% and then a further 25%. How much did she pay for the coat?

16) There are 240 fish in an aquarium. $^1/_3$ of them are salmon and 40% are trout. How many fish are neither salmon or trout?

17) Express $^3/_5$ as a percentage.

18) In the summer a shopkeeper increased the price of sunglasses by 10%. In the winter he then reduced this price by 25%. If the original price was £100, what was the price of the sunglasses in winter?

19) Dad used coupons to make savings on the groceries. The total of £60 is reduced by 15%. How much did he pay?

20) What is 15% of 200?

21) Express $^1/_8$ as a percentage?

22) What percentage of the circles (to the right) are not shaded?

23) What is 45% of £200?

24) What is $^{25}/_{40}$ expressed as a percentage?

25) Which fraction is the equivalent to 80%?

a. $\frac{3}{8}$ b. $\frac{3}{4}$ c. $\frac{8}{11}$ d. $\frac{4}{5}$ e. $\frac{16}{2}$

Mean/Median/Mode

1) Teresa earned these sums over 4 weeks. What was her average weekly earning?

      £82   £105   £110   £104

2) What is the mode of this set of numbers?

    6 2 81 5 5 6 2 5 2 5 8 5

3) The heights of some children are given. What is their median height?

    121cm   138cm   133cm   128cm   130cm

4) The lengths of time some children needed to complete a test in minutes were:

8, 7, 6.5, 3.2, 4, 9, 12, and 4. What was the range of these times?

5) What is the difference between the range and the mean of these numbers:

    5 15 21 17 3 8 8

6) What is the mean of these numbers:

    4 9 25 14 38

7) Which number is missing, if the mode of the list below is 8?

    4 6 8 4 2 6 8

8) Rebecca swam these distances. What was the median distance?

    20m 28m 32m 35m 42m 25m 10m

9) Corrie bought some picture frames of various sizes. What was the range of sizes?

    20cm²   45cm²   56cm²   64cm²   18cm²

10) What is the difference between the mode and the median of these numbers:

    -4 6 2 3 9 9 1 5 -2

11) Over the six weeks of summer cricket, Charlie scored 774 runs. What was the mean score per week?

12) In these games of rounders, what was the mode of the scores?

Game	Score
1	1
2	5
3	2
4	6
5	1
6	8
7	1

13) Find the median of the following numbers:

    0.4 0.004 4.1 4.12 5 5 2

14) Find the range of these scores: 0.08, 5.3, 20.4, 0.12, 9.008

Mean/Median/Mode

15) Find the difference between the mode and the mean of these scores:

        85   90   75   40   85

16) Scrooge was feeling mean, and provided Bob Crachit with an average wage of only £1.60 per month. How much was this per week?

17) What is the mode of the number of sides of these shapes?

    hexagon   triangle   circle   square   pentagon   square   circle   triangle   square   hexagon   square

18) Find the median of these numbers:

    40,002   36,241   17,004   5,246   15,465

19) What is the range between the cube of 4, and the cube of 5?

20) If the average score for a game played once a day, Monday through Friday, is 20, what was the score on Thursday?

    Mon – 15   Tues – 21   Wed – 18   Thu – ?   Fri – 30

21) What is the mean of these football scores?

Game	1	2	3	4	5	6
Score	2	0	4	5	1	0

22) During a week, Miles travelled these distances. What was the mode of the journeys travelled?

    15km   24km   51km   18km   8km   51km

23) Find the median of those numbers:

    3 6 6 2 18 17 7 1 6 2 9

24) Below is a list of train arrival times compared to when they were expected, so 3 would be three minutes early, -3 would be three minutes late. What is the range of these times?

    5   -2   7   -42   1   0   -31

25) What is the mean of these numbers:

    4 11 4 2 5 0 12 6 1

Maths Vocabulary

1) Name a quadrilateral with one pair of parallel sides.

2) What are lines that are always the same distance apart, and never touch?

3) The difference between the lowest and the highest in a list of numbers is called _____?

4) What the number above the line in a fraction called?

5) What is the distance from the centre of a circle to its edge?

6) What is the name of the corner of a shape, where two line segments meet?

7) What is the name of a triangle with two sides of equal length?

8) An angle measured in a clockwise direction from the north is called _____?

9) What is the distance directly across the widest part of a circle?

10) What is the likelihood of something happening in the future?

11) What is the mathematical average of a set of numbers called?

12) Name at least 4 types of angles.

13) What is the name of a nine-sided polygon?

14) What is the product?

15) What is the bottom part of a fraction called?

16) What is the mode?

17) The distance around a circle is called the _____?

18) What is a sector of a circle?

19) What is a polygon?

20) What does perpendicular mean?

21) A triangle with sides of all different lengths is called _____?

22) What is a 'y' axis?

23) What do the angles of an oblong add up to?

24) What is an integer?

25) What does 'not drawn to scale' mean?

Sequences

1)   5, 17, 15, 27, 25, ___

2)   31, 17, 33, 15, 35, ___

3)   6, 9, 7, 10, 8, ___

4)   17, 18, 17, 19, 18, 21, 20, ___

5)   23, 15, 27, 19, 31, ___

6)   2, 10, 40, 120, ___

7)   3, 10, 16, 21, ___

8)   1, 2, 4, 8, 16, 32, ___

9)   39, 30, 22, 15, 9, 4, ___

10)   -10, -5, 2, 7, __

11)   6, 10, 18, 34, 66, __

12)   2, 4, 6, 10, 16, __

13)   1, 8, 5, 11, 7, 12, __

14)   3, 6, 5, 10, 9, 18, 17, __

15)   197, 203, 406, 412, 824, ___

16)   1, 1, 2, 3, 5, 8, 13, __

17)   81, 64, 49, __, 25

18)   2, 6, 24, 120, ___

19)   360, 130, 120, 40, 30, __

20)   200, 100, 120, 20, __

21)   4, 9, 11, 16, 18, __

22)   10, 21, 11, 20, 14, 17, 19, __

23)   1, 2, 4, 7, 11, 16, __

24)   21, 28, 35, 42, __

25)   2, 4, 6, 12, 14, __

Factors and Special Numbers

1) Name the factors of 64

2) What is the 9th prime number?

3) What is the cube of 5?

4) What is the 4th triangular number?

5) Can a prime number be an even number?

6) Is 4 a factor of 62?

7) What are the prime factors of 142?

8) What is the cube of 4, divided by 8?

9) Add together the 3rd square, cube, triangular and prime number

10) Is 1 a prime number?

11) Add the second largest factor of 18 to the second smallest factor of 21. What is the sum?

12) What are the prime numbers between 7 and 14?

13) What is the cube of 4, minus the square of 4?

14) $4^2 + 6^3$

15) If a cube of a number is 64, what is its square?

16) Is 12 a triangular number?

17) What factor of 25 is also a prime number?

18) What is the 4th prime number multiplied by the 3rd square number?

19) Add the first 3 square numbers and divide them by 7.

20) Is 2007 a prime number?

21) What is the lowest common multiple of 12, 27 and 108?

22) What is the 7th prime number?

23) If a number squared is 121, what is its cube?

24) How many prime numbers are there between 1 and 20?

25) What are the prime factors of 60?

Shapes and Symmetry

Note: Diagrams are not to scale

1) What is the area of this shape?

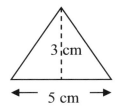

2) Name a regular shape with rotational symmetry of 2

3) How many pairs of parallel lines does a kite have?

4) A regular 2D shape has interior angles that add up to 900°. What is the shape?

5) What is the volume of this triangular prism?

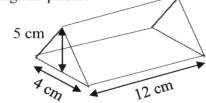

6) What is the area of this shape?

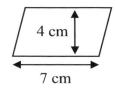

7) How many lines of reflectional symmetry does a parallelogram (that is not a square or rhombus) have?

8) What is the name of a triangle with two equal sides and two equal angles?

9) What do the angles of a triangle and a parallelogram add up to?

10) What is the length of this shape, if the volume is 400 cm³ ?

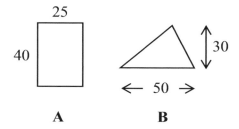

face area = 8 cm²

11) By how much is shape B smaller than shape A in cm² ?

25

40

A

30

← 50 →

B

12) How many lines of reflectional symmetry does an equilateral triangle have?

13) A cylinder has a volume of 480 cm³. If the length is 12 cm, what is the area of the circular face?

Shapes and Symmetry

14) The capacity of a rectangular tank is 960 cm³. Its base is 10 cm x 8 cm, and the water in it measures up to 8 cm. How much more water is needed to fill the tank?

15) How many lines of reflectional symmetry does a scalene triangle have?

16) Is this shape a polyhedron?

17) What is the difference between the rotational order of symmetry of a square, and its number of lines of reflectional symmetry?

18) What is the area of the shaded part of this shape?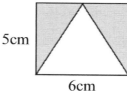

19) What is the name of this polyhedron?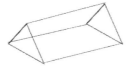

20) The area of the face of a cube is 144 cm². What is the length of a single side?

21) What is the order of rotational symmetry of an octagon?

22) Which of these nets will make a cube when folded?

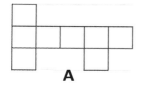   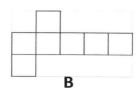   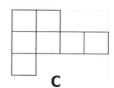   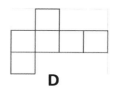

A   B   C   D

23) What shape can this net make?

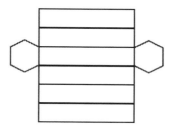

24) The area of one face of a cube is 25 cm². What is the total surface area of the cube?

25) Which shape has more lines of reflectional symmetry, a rhombus (that is not a square) or an equilateral triangle?

Fractions and Ratios

1) $\frac{4}{9} + \frac{2}{27}$

2) There are 27 boys and 9 girls in Ms. Kee's class. What is the simplified ratio of boys to girls?

3) Find $\frac{2}{5}$ of 165

4) Find $\frac{4}{5} \times \frac{2}{3}$ Give your answer in the simplest form.

5) Siobhan found a section of string that was 64 cm long. She cut it into quarters, and then further used only $\frac{1}{8}$ of one of those pieces. What was the length of string she used?

6) $\frac{5}{9} + \frac{3}{7}$

7) Bananas cost 70p per kilogram. What is the cost of 3.5 kg of bananas?

8) A carton contains jars of pickled foods. $\frac{2}{7}$ of the jars are onions, $\frac{2}{3}$ are beetroot, and the rest are eggs. What fraction of the jars are eggs?

9) Fatima found that $\frac{2}{3}$ of $\frac{1}{5}$ is $\frac{1}{15}$. Is she correct?

10) Mia needed to improve her test score by one quarter. If her original test score was 80, what score does she hope to achieve?

11) $\frac{7}{8} + 1\frac{1}{2}$

12) Maria has a recipe for spaghetti that calls for 250 g ground beef, 400 g pasta, and 200 g sauce, to serve two people. How much ground beef will she need to make a dinner for five people?

13) Monty earns £24 working part time. He spends £12.50 on games and £8.50 on food. What fraction of his original £24 will he have left?

14) Express 0.125 as a fraction

15) How many thirds are there in 9?

16) $3\frac{1}{3} + 2\frac{1}{2}$

17) $7\frac{7}{8} - 3\frac{1}{4}$

18) If a pair of earrings that cost £9.21 is reduced by a third, how much will they cost now?

19) $4\left(\frac{1}{3} \times 4\right)$

20) A pot holds red, yellow, and blue pens in the ratio of 4:1:3. If there are 2 yellow pens, how many pens are there in total?

21) $19\frac{3}{4} + \frac{7}{8}$

22) Is $\frac{142}{7}$ greater or less than 21?

23) In a box of 49 chocolates, the ratio of toffee flavoured to all other types of chocolates is 1:6. How many are not toffee flavoured?

24) Ed bought a comic book from the U.S. that cost $10.80. If the pound is worth $1.20, how much did he pay in pounds and pence?

25) Tom buys a packet of 90 mints. He eats one-third of it and then divides the rest amongst his five friends. How many mints does each friend get?

Time

1) How many hours are there in a fortnight?

2) Jade is going to Cornwall from the 23rd of May until the 4th of June. How many days will she be away, including June 4th?

3) How many months have 31 days?

4) Millie took a Maths test. She had 50 minutes to complete 100 questions. On average, how long should she spend on each question?

5) What is the time difference between 8:15am and 9:48pm?

6) When is the next leap year?

7) The time zone difference between London and some other cities is as follows:

New York	London	Nairobi	Tokyo
− 5 hours	0 hours	+ 3 hours	+ 8 hours

   If it is 17:00 in Tokyo, then what time is it in New York?

8) How many seconds is 24 hours?

9) How many months in 5 years?

10) How many days, including 3 leap years, in a decade?

11) If September 4th is on a Tuesday, on what day of the week would September 21st be?

12) How many degrees are there between the hand positions of one o'clock and two o'clock on an analogue clock?

13) Douglas wants to arrive for a concert in Liverpool at 7:00pm. He can either leave with a friend and arrive at 6:45pm or travel on a train. The train leaves at 5:21pm and takes one hour and 42 minutes. Which way would he arrive sooner?

14) Is 3 hours, 14 minutes more or less than 200 minutes?

15) If a bus traveling from Cheltenham to Edinburgh was running 42 minutes late. It left at 9:15am and arrived at 9:19pm. What time would it have arrived, if it had been on time?

16) How many days are in 3 years, including a leap year?

17) Which will arrive sooner, a train travelling at 30mph that must go 120 miles, or a lorry travelling at 20mph that goes 100 miles? (Assume they leave at the same time)

18) It takes Max 4 minutes to make a sandwich. At this rate, how many can he make in one hour?

Time

19) Regina takes 25 minutes to complete an obstacle course. Her friend takes three times as long plus 5 minutes. How long is her friend's time in seconds?

20) Robert is running in a race, in which he must travel 15 kilometres. If he runs at an average speed of 4km per hour, how long will he running, measured in minutes?

21) The yew tree can live to be over 1000 years old. If a yew lives to be 1,530 years olds, how many decades has it lived?

22) If Tia does 30 press-ups per day, how many will she do in a fortnight?

23) A tap fills a tank with water at a rate of 25ml per 30 seconds. If the tank holds one litre, how long will it take to fill the tank?

24) School assembly starts at 8:45am. If Remy walks to school, it usually takes him an hour and ten minutes. What is the latest time Remy can leave if he wants to be at school on time?

25) How long is September, plus one day and one hour in total? Give your answer in hours.

Data & Graphs

1) Mia attended summer camp and made a pie chart showing where the children who attended were from. If there were 50 children in total at the camp, how many were from Wales?

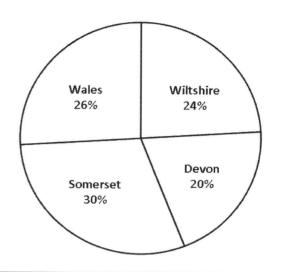

2) How many more children from Somerset attended than from Devon?

Johnny wanted to look at the number of goals his football team had scored in each match this season, so he made the bar graph shown below.

3) How many games has his team played this year?

4) How many goals were scored in total?

5) What was the average number of goals his team scored per game?

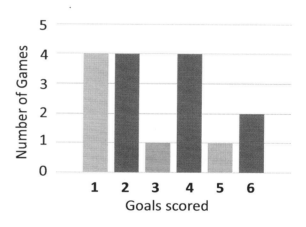

6) A restaurant wanted to see how many customers were coming in at different times. The average number of customers was plotted in the graph to the right. Based on the information, what hour is the busiest at the restaurant?

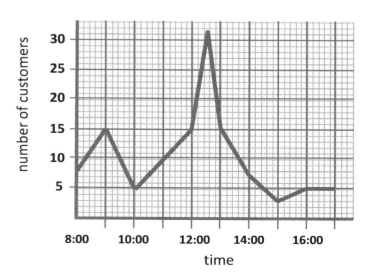

7) At what time are there the least number of customers in the restaurant?

141

Data & Graphs

The timetable below shows regional train times between Birmingham and Manchester.

Birmingham	0620	0635	0650	0705	0720	0745	0800
Wolverhampton	0642	0657	0712	0727	0742	0807	0822
Stafford Station	0656	0711	0746	0741	0756	0821	0836
Stoke-on-Trent	0712	0730	0802	0815	0830	0840	0853
Macclesfield	0735	0755	0827	0837	0852	0903	0915
Stockport		0811		0853			0931
Manchester	0800	0822	0852	0904	0917	0930	0942

8)   Which train is the fastest from Stoke to Manchester? Give the time it leaves Stoke-on-Trent for your answer.

9)   How many minutes longer does it take to go from Birmingham to Manchester on the 0650 train compared to the 0620 train?

10) Gina has an important meeting in Manchester at 0900. If it takes her 15 minutes to get to the meeting from the train station, what is the latest time she should leave from Stoke?

11) Vignesh conducted an experiment and observed the temperature of a substance heated over time. How long did it take for the substance to reach its maximum temperature?

12) What was the temperature after 10 minutes?

13) When was the substance hotter – after 15 minutes or after 50 minutes?

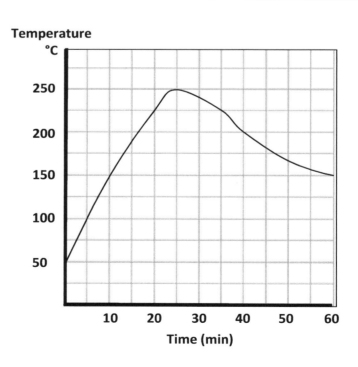

Data & Graphs

Terry asked all of the children in his year group about their favourite flavour of ice cream. He took all 72 of their answers and made the following pie chart:

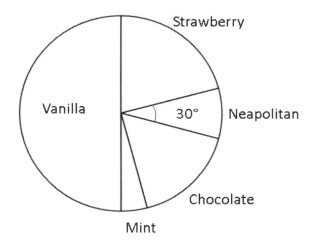

14) If $^1/_2$ of the children liked vanilla, how many of the children liked another flavour?

15) How many of the children liked Neapolitan? (show your answer as a fraction)

16) If mint got 3 votes, and chocolate got 12, how many children voted for strawberry?

Contestant	Time
Jasmine	33.545 sec
Ariel	33.313 sec
Hailey	33.103 sec
Moana	34.240 sec
Daisy	34.616 sec

17) The best times for the 200m race on Sports Day are shown in the table. Who won the race?

18) Rounding to the nearest second, how many finished faster than 34 seconds?

Location	Bottle production
Birmingham	
London	
Manchester	

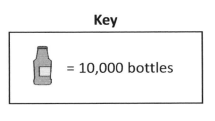

Key

= 10,000 bottles

19) The pictogram shows the amount of bottles that have been produced during the last month at different factories. How many bottles were produced in total?

20) What was the average amount of bottles produced by a factory?

Freya made the Venn diagram below showing what kind of pets her friends own.

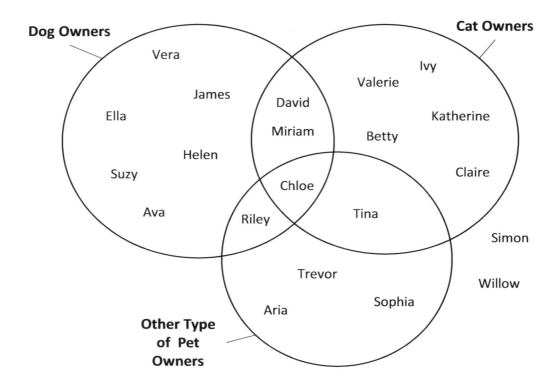

21) How many friends did Freya include in her diagram?

22) What type of pet is most popular among her friends?

23) How many of her friends do not own a cat or a dog?

24) What is the probability that a dog owner will own another type of pet? (express in simplest terms as a fraction)

25) If one of her friends owns a pet other than dog or cat, what is the probability that they will also own a dog or cat? (express as a percentage)

Glossary

Term	Definition
2D	Two dimensional - having only two dimensions, usually length and width
3D	Three dimensional - having three dimensions, usually length, width and depth
acute angle	Any angle that is less than 90°
adjacent angles	Adjacent means next to. Adjacent angles have a common side and a common vertex, but do not overlap. Angle ABC is adjacent to angle CBD
algebra	A branch of Maths where letters are substituted for numbers
alternate angles	one of a pair of angles with different vertices and on opposite sides of a line intersecting two other parallel lines (Z angles) Angles a and d are alternate angles Angles c and b are alternate angles
area	The amount of space within a two-dimensional shape. Formulas to remember are for a <u>triangle</u>: **Area = 1/2 base x height OR base x height divided by 2.** For a <u>rectangle</u>: **Area = height x length**. Area is expressed in square units (such as cm²)
bearing	The angle in degrees measured clockwise from north
brackets	Symbols used in pairs to group things together ( ) { } [ ]
bisect	Divide something into two parts
BODMAS	**B**rackets (parts of a calculation inside brackets always come first), **O**rders (numbers involving powers or square roots), **D**ivision & **M**ultiplication, **A**ddition & **S**ubtraction. Note: **O** can be substituted for **I** – indices
century	A period of one hundred years
circumference	The distance around a circle's edge
complementary angles	Two angles are complementary when they add up to 90 degrees Angles ABC and CBD are complementary angles

145

Glossary

Term	Definition
congruent	Having the same shape and size
conversion	A change in the form of measurement (inches to mm, pounds to kg, etc.)
coordinates	Coordinates are two points on a grid that identify the position of another point. They are always written as (x, y) where **x** is the position on the x-axis and **y** is the position on the y-axis. For example, point (5, 3) is is located five across and three up from the origin (0, 0)
cube number	Any whole number multiplied by itself, and then again by itself (example: $2 \times 2 \times 2 = 2^3$)
cuboid	A 3D shape (polyhedron) made of six quadrilateral sides, placed at 90° angles
decade	A period of ten years
decimal number	A number whose whole number part and the fractional part is separated by a dot (decimal point).
denominator	The bottom part of a fraction. The denominator represents how many parts the whole was divided into.
dodecagon	A 12-sided flat shape
dodecahedron	A 12-sided 3D shape
edge	A line segment that joins two vertices
equilateral triangle	A triangle in which all 3 sides have the same length. All three angles are also equal, at 60°
equivalent	Equal in value, function, or meaning
face	Any of the flat surfaces of a solid object
factor	a number that divides into another number exactly and without leaving a remainder. Example: 1, 2, 4, 8, and 16 are factors of the number 16.
Fibonacci Sequence	A series of numbers where the next number is found by adding up the two numbers before it. (example: 0, 1, 1, 2, 3, 5, 8, 13, 21, …)

146

Glossary

Term	Definition
fraction	A number that represents part of a whole. A fraction with a larger denominator than numerator is called **improper**.
gradient	A number that describes the direction and steepness of a line, also called the slope. $$\text{slope} = \frac{\text{vertical rise}}{\text{horizontal distance}} = \frac{3}{4} \text{ or } 0.75$$ A slope going downhill would be a negative number.
integer	A whole number, without fractions.
isosceles	A triangle with two sides and two angles that are the same.
kite	A polygon that has two pairs of sides next to each other that have equal length. None of the sides of a kite are parallel.
leap year	A year in which February has 29 days - this occurs every four years (example: 2016, 2020, 2024, 2028)
millennium	A period of one thousand years
mirror/reflectional symmetry	A shape has symmetry if a **mirror line** (or line of symmetry) can be drawn where one half mirrors the other. This is also called **reflection symmetry**. **Isosceles Triangle** One line of symmetry **Square** Four lines of symmetry **Circle** Infinite lines of symmetry **Parallelogram** No lines of symmetry **Equilateral Triangle** Three lines of symmetry **Rhombus** Two lines of symmetry **Pentagon** Five lines of symmetry **Irregular Trapezium** No lines of symmetry
mode	The number which appears most often in a set of numbers. 5, 6, **5**, 4, 3, 4, **5**, 2, 7, **5**, 3, 4, **5**, 2, **5**, 3 The number 5 is the mode in the above example

Glossary

Term	Definition
multiple	A whole number that can be divided by another whole number, leaving no remainder when doing so.
net	A two-dimensional pattern that can be folded to create a three-dimensional shape. cube pyramid
numerator	The top part of a fraction. The numerator represents how many parts are left from the whole.
oblong	Any rectangle except a square
obtuse angle	An angle greater than 90°, but less than 180°
octagon	An eight-sided polygon
octahedron	A polyhedron with eight triangular faces. A regular octahedron has eight equilateral triangles.
opposite angles	Opposite angles are non-adjacent angles formed by two intersecting lines. Opposite angles are equal in measure. a = c b = d
parallelogram	A quadrilateral with two pairs of parallel sides. A rhombus and a square are the only parallelograms with reflectional symmetry.
percentage	A number expressed as a fraction of 100. For example, 25% = 0.25, or $^1/_4$
perpendicular	To meet at a 90° angle In this example, the two lines are perpendicular 90°
place value	The value of each digit in a number. (see table below)

Thousands	Hundreds	Tens	Ones	Decimal point	Tenths	Hundredths	Thousandths
5	1	0	3	.	7	8	2

Glossary

Term	Definition
polygon	Any 2-dimensional shape formed with straight lines. A **regular** polygon has sides that are all the same length. Examples are: Equilateral Triangle — 3 sides Square — 4 sides Pentagon — 5 sides Hexagon — 6 sides An **irregular** polygon has sides and/or angles of different sizes. Some examples include: Right-Angled Triangle — 3 sides, 1 angle of 90° Trapezium — 4 sides, 1 pair of parallel sides Parallelogram — 4 sides, 2 pair of parallel sides Rhombus — 4 equal sides, 2 pair of parallel sides
polyhedron	A 3-dimensional solid which consists of a collection of polygons, usually joined at their edges cube pyramid triangular prism Note: Cylinders, Cones & Spheres are not polyhedrons, as they do not have all flat faces.
prime number	A number greater than 1 that can only be divided by 1 and itself. The first twelve prime numbers are **2, 3, 5, 7, 11, 13, 17, 19, 23, 29, 31, 37**

Glossary

Term	Definition
prism	A solid shape with identical ends, flat faces, and the same cross section throughout the shape. A prism is a polyhedron. The ends (bases) of a prism are parallel rectangular prism Prisms are named after their base heptagonal prism
probability	A numerical description of how likely an event is to occur or how likely it is that something is true. Probability can be expressed as a fraction or a percentage.
product	The result of multiplying two numbers (or expressions) together
quadrant	One of the four quarters of the coordinate plane, with the x- and y-axis dividing into four quadrants y-axis Quadrant IV Quadrant I x-axis -5 -4 -3 -2 -1 1 2 3 4 5 Quadrant III Quadrant II
quadrilateral	A two-dimensional shape with four straight sides. Quadrilaterals include: parallelogram, square, rhombus, rectangle, kite and trapezium
quotient	The answer after dividing one number by another
range	The difference between the highest and the lowest values in a set
ratio	A comparison of two or more numbers, indicating the relative numerical value to each other. In this example, the ratio of oranges to bananas is 5 : 3

Glossary

Term	Definition
reflex angle	An angle whose measure is greater than 180 degrees but smaller than 360 degrees reflex angle greater than 180° less than 360°
rhombus	A flat shape with 4 equal straight sides. Opposite angles are equal. A rhombus looks like a diamond. It is also a parallelogram.
right angle	An angle that measures 90°
rotational symmetry	When a shape can be rotated around a centre point and the object appears the same. The **order of rotational symmetry** is the number of times the shape will repeat itself throughout a 360° rotation. 1 2 A rectangle repeats itself twice in a 360° rotation so it has a rotational symmetry order of 2. *If a shape cannot repeat itself then it has a rotational symmetry of 1.* **Trapezium** rotational symmetry order of 1 **Parallelogram** rotational symmetry order of 2 **Equilateral Triangle** rotational symmetry order of 3 **Hexagon** rotational symmetry order of 6 Note that the order of rotational symmetry is different than the number of lines of reflectional symmetry for some polygons
rounding	Replacing a number with an approximate value that is easier to use in calculations. For example: Round 55,455 to the nearest thousand. Answer : 55,000
scalene	A triangle with all sides of different lengths (and all angles of different measures)
sector	A 'pie-slice' portion of a circle
sequence	A group of numbers that have a relationship or pattern that determines the order of the numbers.

Term	Definition
square number	Any whole number multiplied by itself
straight angle	An angle that measures 180° (a straight line)
transformation	A process that moves a polygon or other two-dimensional object on a plane or coordinate system. The three types of transformation are **translation**, **rotation**, and **reflection** Translation is simply moving a shape to a new location without making any changes to the shape. Rotation is the turning of a shape around a point. Rotation can be either clockwise or anticlockwise Reflection is a mirror image, just as you would see as if looking in a mirror. In the examples to the right, the y-axis is serving as the mirror line. Shape A is the reflection of shape B, and shape C is the reflection of shape D.
trapezium	A quadrilateral with one pair of sides parallel

Glossary

Term	Definition
Venn diagram	A diagram that shows relationships between sets of data, displayed as circles
vertex	A corner, or the angular point of a shape (plural - vertices) vertices
volume	The amount of space inside a shape. For cubes and cuboids, the volume can be calculated by multiplying the length, width (or depth) and height. The volume is always expressed in cubed units. 5cm 2cm 9cm length = 9cm height = 5cm width = 2cm volume = 9 x 5 x 2 = 90 volume = 90cm³ Note that this is the same as multiplying the area of one of the faces times the length.
whole number	A number without fractions

153

Answer Key

In Reflection, Page 24

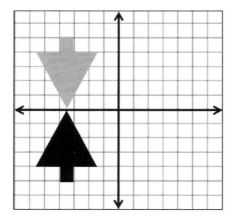

1) The Tree
   x-axis

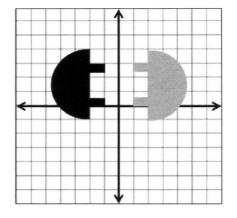

2) The Bug
   y-axis

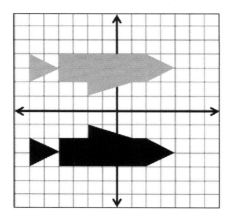

3) The Fish
   x-axis

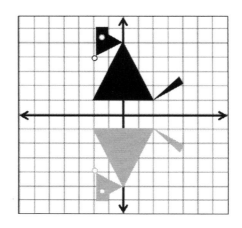

4) The Dog
   x-axis

Crack the Code, Page 25

Symbol	Value	Symbol	Value
✉	= 1	▣	= 7
△	= 2	⬭	= 8
⊕	= 3	∟	= 9
★	= 4	⬇	= 10
◆	= 5	♡	= 11
▭	= 6	◗	= 12

Fractions Snap!, Pages 26-30

$$\frac{1}{4} = \frac{2}{8} = \frac{3}{12} = \frac{4}{16}$$

$$\frac{1}{2} = \frac{5}{10} = \frac{9}{18} = \frac{7}{14}$$

$$\frac{3}{4} = \frac{6}{8} = \frac{9}{12} = \frac{15}{20}$$

$$\frac{2}{3} = \frac{6}{9} = \frac{12}{18} = \frac{20}{30}$$

$$\frac{4}{5} = \frac{8}{10} = \frac{12}{15} = \frac{16}{20}$$

$$\frac{1}{8} = \frac{3}{16} = \frac{3}{24} = \frac{4}{32}$$

$$\frac{1}{7} = \frac{2}{14} = \frac{3}{21} = \frac{5}{35}$$

$$\frac{5}{9} = \frac{10}{18} = \frac{20}{36} = \frac{25}{45}$$

$$\frac{3}{8} = \frac{6}{16} = \frac{15}{40} = \frac{21}{56}$$

$$\frac{5}{6} = \frac{10}{12} = \frac{15}{18} = \frac{20}{24}$$

$$\frac{1}{12} = \frac{4}{48} = \frac{6}{72} = \frac{7}{84}$$

$$\frac{5}{4} = 1\frac{1}{4} = \frac{10}{8} = 1\frac{4}{16}$$

Answer Key

Mystery Wheels, Page 31

a. 21 – the numbers increase by 3 going clockwise starting with 3

b. 27 – the numbers increase by 4 going anticlockwise starting with 7

c. 30 – the numbers increase by 15 going clockwise starting with -5

d. 21 – the numbers are triangular numbers going anticlockwise starting with 1

e. 25 – the numbers are squares going clockwise starting from 1

f. 17 – the wheel has prime numbers going anticlockwise starting from 2

g. 25 – starting from 1, the numbers go clockwise alternating between adding 20 and subtracting 3

h. 125 – starting from 0, the numbers are cube numbers going clockwise

i. 2 – the numbers opposite one another must add up to 12

Missing Operators, Page 36-37

1) $(7 + 2) \div 3 = 3$

2) $(1 \times 4) + 2 = 6$

3) $(5 + 5) \times 5 = 50$

4) $(8 - 5) \times 6 = 18$

5) $12 \times 2 + 6 = 30$

6) $(25 - 4) \div 7 = 3$

7) $100 \div 10 - 4 = 6$

8) $(4 + 5) \times 3 = 27$

9) $3 \times (7 - 5) + 1 = 7$

10) $(35 + 7) \div 3 - (2 \times 3) = 8$ or
$(35 \div 7) - 3 + (2 \times 3) = 8$

11) $(15 - 11) \times 3 \div (2 + 4) = 2$

12) $(6 \times 6) \div 2 - 8 + 4 = 14$

Sneaky Sequences, Pages 43-45

1) 18 – pattern is +1, +2, +3, +4, +5

2) 6 – pattern is multiply by 2

3) 25 – pattern is to divide by 5

4) 17 – pattern is –7, –6, –5, –4, –3

5) 4 – pattern is they are square numbers 1, 4, 9, 16, 25, 36

6) 48 – the pattern skips/alternates numbers starting with x2, then +5

7) The total is **52**. Meg and Shauna will make 2 more each hour, so the pattern is 10, 12, 14, 16 (10+12+14+16 = 52)

8) He will receive **320** on Friday – doubling each day the pattern is 20, 40, 80, 160, 320.

9) It will take **five weeks**. Eva will reduce by 80 minutes each week to 1180 in the first week, then 1100, 1020, 940, and finally 860 by the fifth week. The goal of 15 hours is 900 minutes (60 x 15).

155

Answer Key

Sneaky Sequences, Pages 43-45 (continued)

10) The prize will be **£32.2 million** in week 10. The pattern is for the prize to go up by £6 million, then down by £2 million. (10.2, 16.2, 14.2, 20.2, 18.2, 24.2, 22.2, 28.2, 26.2, 32.2)

11) For each square added, there are two diamonds added. So there will be **2n + 2** diamonds where n is the nth term (n = number of squares). Therefore **14 diamonds** when there are 6 squares, and **26 diamonds** when there are 12 squares.

12) **d** - The pattern in the grid rows is +2, -1, +1 going left to right; and -3, +2, +1 in the columns going down

4	6	5	6
1	3	2	3
3	5	4	5
4	6	5	6

Shapes & Symmetry Bingo, pages 46-51

What is a six-sided polygon called? **hexagon**

What shape has fewer lines of reflectional symmetry: an equilateral triangle, or a rhombus? **rhombus**

What is an eight-sided polygon called? **octagon**

What is another word for having the same shape and size? **congruent**

What is the name of a shape that has 3 equal angles and 3 lines of reflectional symmetry? **equilateral triangle**

What is the number of edges in a cuboid minus the number of its vertices? **4**

What are the number of faces of a pentagonal prism? **7**

When two lines cross at a right angle, what can they be called? **perpendicular**

Find the 3D shape on your card that has no vertices – **cylinder**

What is the number of lines of symmetry in a parallelogram, that is not a rhombus or a square? **0**

What is the measure of each angle in an equilateral triangle? **60°**

Does a parallelogram (that is not a square) have an order of rotational symmetry of 2? **Yes**

What is the order of rotational symmetry of a kite? **1**

When an isosceles triangle has one angle that equals 90°, what is the size of each of the other two angles? **45**

What is the name of a 2D pattern, that can be folded to create a 3D shape? **net**

What is the name of two lines, who are always the same distance apart? **parallel**

A rectangle has four angles that all measure _____ degrees - **90**

What is a line called, that goes from one side of a circle to the other, that passes through the centre? **diameter**

How many vertices does a cuboid have? **8**

Shapes & Symmetry Bingo, pages 46-51 (continued)

What is the number of vertices in a triangular prism? **6**

Does an isosceles triangle always have a 90° angle? **no**

What is a 3-dimensional solid which consists of a collection of polygons, usually joined at their edges? **polyhedron**

How many equal angles does an isosceles triangle have? **2**

What is the name of a triangle that has unequal sides? **scalene**

What Was the Question? page 61

1) What are the sum of the angles in a quadrilateral?

2) What is a 9-sided polygon called?

3) What is a shape with four equal sides called?

4) What is $1/8$ expressed as a decimal?

5) What is a three-dimensional shape, containing six equal squares?

6) What are the sum of the angles in a triangle, <u>or</u> what are the sum of the angles along a straight line?

7) What is a Fibonacci sequence?

8) What is the Roman Numeral for 50?

9) What are the factors of 12?

10) What does each angle measure in an equilateral triangle?

11) What is the distance around the outside of a shape called?

12) What are 10 km expressed as metres?

13) What is an angle whose measure is greater than 180 degrees but smaller than 360 degrees?

14) What are the first six triangular numbers?

15) What is a seven-sided polygon called?

16) What is 1059 written in Roman Numerals?

17) What is the square of 5?

18) What is the area of a triangle?

19) What is a straight line passing from side to side through the centre of a circle?

20) What do you call the corner of a shape, where two line segments meet?

21) What is one litre expressed in millilitres?

22) What is 60%, expressed as a fraction?

23) What is a term for the relative size of two or more values?

24) What is the amount of space a 3D shape takes up called?

25) What is a number that divides into another number exactly and without leaving a remainder.?

Answer Key

Symbol Addition, pages 62-63

1. = 5 / = 2 / = 8

2. 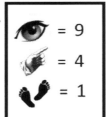 = 2 / = 0 / = 4

3. 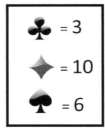 = 9 / = 4 / = 1

4. 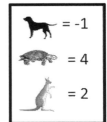 = 3 / = 10 / = 6

5. = -1 / = 4 / = 2

6.  = 0 / = 2 / = 10

7.  = 6 / = 3 / = -2

Square Master, page 65   There are 19 squares. By size:

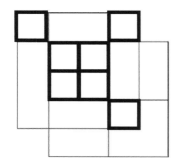

7 single block squares
(1x1)

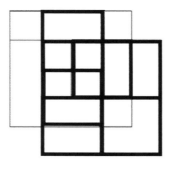

7 four-block squares
(2x2)

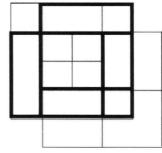

3 nine-block squares
(3x3)

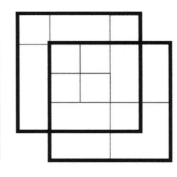

2 sixteen-block squares
(4x4)

Cube Puzzles, pages 66-68

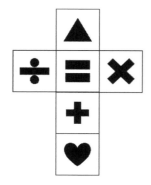

1.

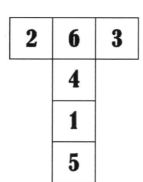

2.

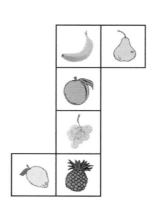

3. b

Cube Puzzles, pages 66 – 68 (continued)

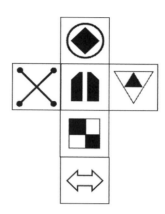

4. c

5. d

Number Logic Puzzle, page 69

	2		8	1	4	0	3		2	5	5
7	5	9	2	4			1	9	9	9	
	0		7	4	5	9		2		8	
7	1	3	8	9		8		4	7	6	8
		6		3	4	9	2	2		1	8
2	0	5	1			3		3	2	2	
4			7		9	1	1	1		9	
4	5	5	3	5			9		2		5
7		1	2		7	9	5		6		0
		1	0	4	3		3	9	9	7	1
6		0			1		5		1		
3	8	4	8		2	2		8	4	8	

Act Your Age, page 73

1) Max is 33, Martin is 11.

2) This year he is 48 (6 x 8), next year he'll be 49 (7 x 7)

3) She will be 64 years old.

4) Lonnie was 25 (5^2) last year, and will be 27 (3^3) next year. So he is 26 now.

5) Ali is 12. Use the equation $2(n-4) = n+4$ to solve for his age

6) The combined age will be 20.

7) 72 years old

8) 49 years old

9) Julius will be 24 years old. Solve for the sister's age $s = 7 \times 5 = 35$. That will be 14 years from now, at which point Julius will be 24.

10) Emily is the youngest

Answer Key

Minesweeper, page 77

0	0	1	**X**
2	2	3	2
X	**X**	2	**X**
2	2	2	1

1.

X	2	2	2
1	2	**X**	**X**
1	2	2	2
X	1	0	0

2.

X	2	2	**X**
2	**X**	3	2
2	3	**X**	1
X	2	1	1

3.

1	2	2	1	0	0	0
1	**X**	**X**	1	0	1	1
1	3	4	3	2	2	**X**
0	1	**X**	**X**	1	**X**	2
1	2	3	2	3	2	2
1	**X**	2	1	3	**X**	2
1	1	2	**X**	3	**X**	2

4.

Sudoku, pages 78-79

3	4	7	8	9	1	2	5	6
8	6	5	7	2	4	3	9	1
9	2	1	6	3	5	7	4	8
6	9	2	5	1	8	4	3	7
7	3	8	4	6	2	9	1	5
1	5	4	3	7	9	8	6	2
4	8	9	1	5	7	6	2	3
2	1	6	9	8	3	5	7	4
5	7	3	2	4	6	1	8	9

Puzzle 1

7	6	3	2	5	8	9	1	4
2	5	1	9	4	6	7	8	3
4	9	8	3	7	1	6	2	5
8	3	2	6	1	5	4	9	7
9	4	6	7	8	2	3	5	1
1	7	5	4	3	9	8	6	2
5	8	7	1	6	3	2	4	9
3	1	9	8	2	4	5	7	6
6	2	4	5	9	7	1	3	8

Puzzle 2

5	4	3	2	7	6	9	8	1
1	2	8	9	4	3	7	6	5
6	9	7	5	8	1	3	4	2
7	3	1	8	5	9	4	2	6
2	8	5	3	6	4	1	7	9
4	6	9	1	2	7	5	3	8
8	7	4	6	9	5	2	1	3
9	1	6	4	3	2	8	5	7
3	5	2	7	1	8	6	9	4

Puzzle 3

Symbolic Scales, pages 80-83

1) From the first example, one octopus = three starfish; from the second example, one starfish = two seahorses; therefore one octopus = six seahorses. The answer is **ten seahorses** will be needed to balance the octopus and two starfish.

2) From the first example, we see that one cap = two party hats; in the second example, one Trilby = four party hats; therefore the answer is that **one Trilby hat** will be needed to balance the two caps.

3) From the first example, one banana = four cherries; from the second example, one pumpkin = ten cherries; the answer is **fourteen cherries** will be needed to balance the one banana and one pumpkin; because we know two bananas and two cherries will balance one pumpkin, the answer is that **three bananas** will be needed to balance the pumpkin and two cherries.

4) From the first example, one panda = seven teddy bears, therefore the answer is that **fifteen teddy bears** will be needed to balance the two pandas and one bear; from the second example, one elephant = two pandas and one teddy bear (or fifteen teddy bears in total). Therefore the answer is that **three pandas** will be needed to balance the elephant and six teddy bears (or 21 teddy bears).

Answer Key

The Need for Speed Game, Pages 84 – 86

1) Side A (443 minutes < 500 minutes)

2) Side B (75 hours < 76 hours)

3) Side A (92 days < 101 days)

4) Side B (720 hours < 751 hours)

5) Side A (864,001 seconds < 864,100 seconds)

6) Side A (2,000 minutes < 2,880 minutes)

7) Side B (199 minutes < 200 minutes)

8) Side B (120 days < 121 days)

9) Side A (2 hours < 2 hours and 10 minutes)

10) Side B (8 hours, 4 minutes < 8 hours, 19 minutes)

11) Side A (30 days < 31 days)

12) Side A (12 years < 20 years)

Bonus – the **shortest** time is Card 9, Side A (two hours). The **longest** is Card 12, Side B (20 years)

A Tangle of Rectangles, page 87

1	2
3	4	5
6	7	8

A total of **20** rectangles can be found in the shape.

From the 8 individual rectangles the following further rectangles can be made:

6 - two block rectangles (1+2, 3+4, 4+5, 1+3, 6+7, 7+8)

3 - three block rectangles (2+4+5, 3+4+5, 6+7+8)

1 - five block rectangle (1+2+3+4+5)

1 - six block rectangles (3+4+5+6+7+8)

1 - eight block rectangle (all combined)

161

161

Answer Key

Maths Vocabulary Word Search, pages 88 – 89

1) face
2) scalene
3) mean
4) adjacent
5) median
6) area
7) parallel
8) circumference
9) acute
10) congruent
11) isosceles
12) ratio
13) cylinder
14) radius
15) prime
16) coordinate
17) numerator
18) polygon
19) century
20) integer

```
A S A Y C E C N E R E F M U C R I C
O C P R I M E T D O L C E G O P G R
T A U U Y A W O L U O D A S O B U C
W L L T H D I N T E G E R J R S Y O
Y E A N E J S M W G R A P B D L M L
R I Y E A N O O R A D I S D I A G R
T L D C O I S B A I O U R N N H E Q
S I Y D T Z C I U N Y N D L A S Y N
C W P A N M E S Q M I E C P T O L T
A Y R S B G L O K N R F A C E B I N
L H O U W L E E M O C D Z Y U R A E
E N T S I G S L I G E F K W G I S C
N I A G H W M L B Y O R O M D B E A
E O R X P A R A L L E L E N E S M T J
G E E Q G L E N S O R W M A U E A D A
N U M B E R Y R T P E A R N R A R
O A U O V W J V A Q O U P A E S E U
C O N G R U E N T C A R A E R R M Y
```

Maths Crossword, pages 90 – 91

4	9			1		1	3	3	5
	9		3	2	5	6		2	0
1	4	5		4	4		2		
		1	6				2	6	4
	2	7		6		2			
1	0		4	2	0	0	2	9	7
3							4		
2	4	7	6		1	0	1		6
	4	2		7	5		4	2	0
		6	2	7	1	4		8	

Magic Squares, pages 92 – 93

8	3	4
1	5	9
6	7	2

a.

16	9	14
11	13	15
12	17	10

b.

63	56	61
58	60	62
59	64	57

c.

162

Answer Key

Magic Squares, pages 92 – 93

13	6	11
8	10	12
9	14	7

d.

10	3	8
5	7	9
6	11	4

e.

18	11	16
13	15	17
14	19	12

f.

18	4	5	15
7	13	12	10
11	9	8	14
6	16	17	3

g.

15	22	-1	6	13
21	3	5	12	14
2	4	11	18	20
8	10	17	19	1
9	16	23	0	7

h.

35	26	1	19	6	24
8	17	28	10	33	15
3	21	32	23	7	25
30	12	5	14	34	16
31	22	9	27	2	20
4	13	36	18	29	11

i.

What Can You See, pages 94 – 95

1) 3 aliens, 4 cows

2) 2 cats, 3 owls

3) 5 guppies, 8 mollies

4) 4 children, 6 robots

5) 4 foxes, 9 badgers

Show Me the Money, pages 96 – 97

1)   c. 4275 Euros.

    They will be staying 21 days. So the cost is 21 times 200 (4200), plus 75 for the cleaning.

2)   d. $3 + \frac{1}{2}e$

    Note that 50p = £0.50, or $\frac{1}{2}$

3)   Mary had the equipment for 12 weeks.

    The total cost $193 = 25 + 14w$, therefore $168 = 14w$, and $w = 12$

4)   1.5kg

    The recipe calls for $m = \frac{2}{8}$ kg per person, or 0.25 kg, therefore 6 x 0.25 = 1.5

5)   She left £1,000,000 in total.

    Wilf received half, or .5T; Rachel received half of Wilf's, or .25T; The cousin got .2T

    Substituting known facts: T = (.5T) + (.25T) + (.2T) + 50,000 (money to charity)

    T = 1,000,000

Answer Key

Show Me the Money, pages 96 – 97 (continued)

6)   The meal cost £32

Solve for the cost of the meal M. The total spent was £48 (£50 - £2 remaining)

$48 = M + .5M$, so $48 = 1.5M$, so £32 = M. The taxi was half the cost, or £16

Weighty Matters, pages 99 – 104

Length

6 kilometres is longer than 60,000 centimetres

1200 metres is longer than 12,000 centimetres

10 metres is longer than 1000 millimetres

2.5 centimetres is shorter than 0.0025 kilometres

39 centimetres is shorter than 3900 millimetres

1.2676 kilometres is shorter than 12,726 metres

Weight

10 tonnes is heaver than 1000 kilograms

1 kilogram is heavier than 100,000 milligrams

0.6 grams is heavier than 60 milligrams

1 tonne weighs less than 10,000,000 grams

99 milligrams weighs less than 0.99 grams

5 grams weighs less than 55,000 milligrams

Volume

1 litre is more than 100 millilitres

5,250 millilitres is more than 5 litres

70,000 millilitres is more than 8 litres

1200 millilitres is less than 1.201 litres

7.1 litres is less than 7,400 millilitres

4,990 millilitres is less than 49 litres

Imperial

500 miles (805 km) is longer than 500 km

25 cm (9.8 inches) is shorter than 25 inches

2 pints (1.1 litres) is more than one litre

2 metres (6.6 feet) is longer than 5 feet

500 ml (0.88 pints) is less than one pint

10 miles (16 km) is shorter than 20 km

The Nth Term Game, pages 109 – 114

Formula	1	2	3	4	5	6	7	8	9	10
2n + 7	9	11	13	15	17	19	21	23	25	27
3n - 2	1	4	7	10	13	14	19	22	25	28
n +24	25	26	27	28	29	30	31	32	33	34
8n/4	2	4	6	8	10	12	14	16	18	20
7n - 3	4	11	18	25	32	39	46	53	60	67
3n x 3	9	18	27	36	45	54	63	72	81	90
5n + 2	7	12	17	22	27	32	37	42	47	52
10n - 5	5	15	25	35	45	55	65	75	85	95
9n/3	3	6	9	12	15	18	21	24	27	30
6n +3	9	15	21	27	33	39	45	51	57	63
4n -3	1	5	9	13	17	21	25	29	33	37
2n x 5	10	20	30	40	50	60	70	80	90	100

Answer Key

Number Analogies, pages 116 – 117

1) 19 (add 3)

2) 49 (square of the number)

3) 12 (divide by 5)

4) 16 (subtract 15)

5) 720 (sum of the interior angles)

6) 36 (t = 6)

7) 75% (the number is the expressed percentage of the fraction, $\frac{3}{5}$ is 60%)

8) 8300 (multiply by 1000)

9) 100 (the relationship is half, if 40% is 200, then 20% would be 100)

10) $\frac{45}{5}$ (the same as the number expressed as a fraction)

11) 16:54 (the time is 13 hours and 50 minutes ahead)

12) Nov (November is the month that has 30 days)

13) 80% (the number is the fraction expressed as a percentage)

14) 156 (multiply times 12)

15) 125 (is the cube of the number)

16) 40% (double the fraction, expressed as a percentage)

17) 81 (square of the number)

18) 18 (multiply by 1.5)

19) 06:00 (12 hours ahead on a 24-hour clock)

20) $\frac{12}{15}$ (percentage expressed as a fraction)

REVIEW QUESTIONS

Four Operations, Page 125

1) £28

2) 14.662

3) 4051

4) 175.75

5) 9901

6) 21 litres (1 litre = 1000 ml)

7) 3006.96

8) −37

9) 3200

10) 2.1

11) 5760

12) 4075g

13) −12

14) 3060

15) 27,300,500

16) £4.50 each (108 ÷ 24 = 4.5)

17) 5.8

18) 8

19) 49.7

20) 24.95

21) 1.6 m

22) 19.03

23) 0.94

24) 3108

25) 12

Answer Key

Algebra, page 126

1) 63
2) 5.5
3) 8a
4) £75
5) y = 12
6) t = 3
7) d = 15
8) 10a + 2b (or 2b + 10a)
9) m = 4
10) t + 2s + 2k
11) y = 5
12) b = 3
13) 8a + 14

14) No, 3(2a + b) = 6a + 3b
15) n = 12
16) j = 16
17) 72
18) £31.50
19) 72
20) 96 – 2R
21) n = 7
22) x = 16
23) 36
24) 0
25) $12q^2$

Angles and Direction, page 127 – 128

1) Two angles are complementary when they add up to 90 degrees
2) Z
3) 74°
4) 225 degrees
5) From the North
6) An angle whose measure is greater than 180 degrees but smaller than 360 degrees
7) Opposite angles are equal
8) 62°
9) East
10) clockwise
11) An angle greater than 90° but less than 180°
12) 145° (180 – 35 = 145)
13) 38°
14) 80° each (360 – 200 = 160, 160 ÷ 2 = 80)
15) 135 degrees
16) 360 degrees
17) 38° (180 – 90 – 52 = 38)
18) 337° (540 – 54 – 47 – 102 = 337)
19) 35°
20) 220 degrees (180 + 40 = 220)
21) 720°
22) 102° (360 – 90 – 110 – 14 – 44 = 102)
23) 342°
24) p = 95° (2p + 170 = 360)
25) NW

166

Probability, page 129

1) $^1/_2$

2) $^4/_{11}$

3) Probability is $^1/_8$ ($^1/_2$ x $^1/_2$ x $^1/_2$)

4) $^1/_4$

5) $^3/_{51}$

6) $^6/_{13}$ (Prime numbers are 2, 3, 5, 7, 11, 13)

7) $^1/_{12}$

8) $^1/_{365}$

9) $^1/_{10}$ (52 cards – 12 face cards = 40 remaining) $^4/_{40}$ = $^1/_{10}$

10) One way – with two sixes

11) $^1/_3$ ($^4/_6$ x $^1/_2$ = $^4/_{12}$)

12) $^2/_5$

13) $^1/_2$

14) $^1/_{25}$ ($^1/_5$ x $^1/_5$ = $^1/_{25}$)

15) $^1/_{13}$

16) $^1/_8$ ($^1/_2$ x $^1/_2$ x $^1/_2$)

17) $^4/_5$

18) $^1/_4$ ($^1/_2$ x $^1/_2$)

19) $^1/_2$

20) $^{11}/_{14}$ ($^2/_7$ + $^1/_2$ = $^{11}/_{14}$)

21) $^1/_2$

22) $^4/_9$

23) $^1/_{20}$ ($^1/_2$ x $^1/_{10}$ = $^1/_{20}$)

24) $^1/_2$

25) $^9/_{10}$ (60 – 6 = 54 pages without pictures, or $^{54}/_{60}$)

Percentages, page 130

1) **£40** (50 x .20 = 10, 50 – 10 = 40)

2) **37.5%**

3) **£32** (40 x .20 = 8, 40 – 8 = 32)

4) **30%**

5) **It cost £21,000.** (.05 x 20,000 = 1,000)

6) **19.5%**

7) **12.5%** (.25 x .50 = 0.125)

8) **31.3** (100 – 68.7 = 31.3)

9) **52% left** (($\frac{2}{5} = \frac{10}{25}$) + $\frac{2}{25}$ = $\frac{12}{25}$ = 0.48 eaten)

10) **6%** (.1 x .6 = .06)

11) **60% are boys** ($\frac{18}{30} = \frac{3}{5}$ = 0.60)

12) **7.2** (18 x .4 = 7.2)

13) **£21.60** (60 x .64 = 38.4, 60 – 38.4 = 21.6)

14) **£340** (400 x .15 = 60, 400 – 60 = 340)

15) **£33.75** (50 x .90 = 45, 45 x .75 = 33.75)

16) **64** (salmon = $^{240}/_3$ = 80, trout = .4 x 240 = 96, other = 240 – (80+96) = 64)

17) **60%**

18) **£82.50** (100 x 1.10 = 110, 110 x .25 = 27.5, 110 – 27.5 = 82.50)

19) **£51** (.15 x 60 = 9, 60 – 9 = 51)

20) **30** (.15 x 200 = 30)

21) **12.5%**

22) **75% are not shaded** ($^9/_{12}$ = 0.75)

23) **£90** (.45 x 200 = 90)

24) **62.5%** ($\frac{25}{40} = \frac{5}{8}$ = 0.625)

25) **d** ($\frac{4}{5}$ = 80%)

Answer Key

Mean/Median/Mode, pages 131 – 132

1) £100.25
2) 5
3) 130cm
4) 8.8 minutes (12 – 3.2)
5) 7 (range = 18, mean = 11)
6) 18
7) 8
8) 28m
9) 46 (64 – 18)
10) 6 (mode = 9, median = 3)
11) 129 runs
12) 1
13) 4.1
14) 20.32 (20.4 – 0.08)
15) 10 (mode = 85, mean = 75)
16) 40p
17) 4
18) 17,004
19) 61 ($4^3 = 64$, $5^3 = 125$)
20) 16 ($84 + t = 20 \times 5$, $t = 100 - 84 = 16$)
21) 2
22) 51km
23) 6
24) 49 minutes (-42 – 7)
25) 5

Maths Vocabulary, page 133

1) A parallelogram or a trapezium
2) parallel
3) the range
4) the numerator
5) the radius
6) the vertex
7) An isosceles triangle
8) a bearing
9) diameter
10) probability
11) the mean
12) acute, obtuse, straight, right, alternate, complementary, reflex, adjacent, opposite
13) nonagon
14) it is the result of two factors being multiplied together
15) the denominator
16) The number which appears most often in a set of numbers
17) circumference
18) A pie-shaped part of a circle
19) a two-dimensional shape that can be formed with at least 3 straight lines and 3 angles
20) Two lines that meet at a 90° angle
21) scalene
22) a vertical axis
23) 360°
24) a number without fractions, a whole number
25) It means that everything was not drawn to its' proper size. A map drawn to scale will have all of the landmarks in a proportionate distance and position from each other.

Answer Key

Sequences, page 134

1) **37** (+12, –2, +12, –2 pattern)

2) **13** (Alternating patterns of +2 and –2)

3) **11** (+3, –2, +3, –2 pattern)

4) **24** (Alternating patterns of +0, +1, +2 and +1, +2, +3)

5) **23** (–8, +12, –8, +12 pattern)

6) **240** (x5, x4, x3, x2 pattern)

7) **25** (+7, +6, +5, +4 pattern)

8) **64** (x2 pattern)

9) **0** (–9, –8, –7, –6, –5, –4 pattern)

10) **14** (+5, +7, +5, +7 pattern)

11) **130** (+4, +8, +16, +32, +64 pattern)

12) **26** (Fibonacci, add the previous two numbers together)

13) **7** (alternating patterns of +7, +6, +5 and –3, –4, –5)

14) **34** (alternating pattern of x2 and –1)

15) **830** (alternating pattern of +6 and x2)

16) **21** (Fibonacci, add the previous two numbers together)

17) **36** (pattern is squares of 9, 8, 7, 6, 5)

18) **720** (pattern is x3, x4, x5, x6)

19) **10** (÷3, –10, ÷3, –10, ÷3 pattern)

20) **40** (–100, +20, –100, +20 pattern)

21) **23** (+5, +2, +5, +2, +5 pattern)

22) **12** (alternating patterns of +1, +3, +5 and –1, –3, –5)

23) **22** (pattern is +1, +2, +3, +4, +5)

24) **49** (pattern is +7)

25) **28** (alternating patterns of x2 and +2)

Factors and Special Numbers, page 135

1) 1, 2, 4, 8, 16, 32, and 64

2) 23

3) 125

4) 10

5) Yes – 2 is a prime number

6) No – the factors of 62 are 1, 2, 31 and 62)

7) The prime factors are 2 and 71

8) 8 (64 ÷ 8 = 8)

9) 47 (9 + 27 + 6 + 5 = 47)

10) No

11) 12 (9 + 3 = 12)

12) 11 and 13

13) 48 (64 – 16 = 48)

14) 232 (216 + 16 = 232)

15) 16 – The cube of 4 is 64. 4 x 4 = 16)

16) No (10 and 15 are, but not 12)

17) 5

18) 63 (7 x 9 = 63)

19) 2 ($1^2 + 2^2 + 3^2 = 14$; 14 ÷ 7 = 2)

20) No (According to the divisibility rules, the sum of the digits [2+0+0+7 = 9] is divisible by 3. So it cannot be a prime number)

21) 3

22) 17

23) 1,331 (11 x 11 = 121)

24) 8 (they are 2, 3, 5, 7, 11, 13, 17, 19)

25) 2, 3, 5 (The factors of 60 are 1, 2, 3, 4, 5, 6, 10, 12, 15, 20, 30, and 60)

Answer Key

Shapes and Symmetry, pages 136 – 137

1) 7.5 cm² ($^1/_2$ x 5 x 3 = 7.5)

2) A rectangle, rhombus, or a parallelogram

3) None

4) A heptagon

5) 120 cm³

6) 28 cm²

7) None

8) An isosceles triangle

9) 540° (180 + 360)

10) 50 cm

11) 250 cm² (1000 – 750)

12) Three

13) 40 cm² (480 ÷ 12 = 40)

14) Another 4cm, <u>or</u> 320 cm³ volume of water

15) None

16) No, a polyhedron must only have straight lines

17) No difference – both are 4

18) 15 cm² (area of rectangle – area of the triangle; 30 – 15 = 30)

19) triangular prism

20) 12 cm (144 is the square of 12)

21) 8

22) D

23) a hexagonal prism

24) 150 cm² (25 x 6 = 150)

25) The equilateral triangle (3 lines) – the rhombus has two.

Fractions and Ratios, page 138

1) $\frac{14}{27}$

2) The simplified ratio of boys to girls is 3:1

3) 66

4) $\frac{8}{15}$

5) 2 cm (64 x $\frac{1}{4}$ x $\frac{1}{8}$ = 2)

6) $\frac{62}{63}$ ($\frac{35}{63}+\frac{27}{63}=\frac{62}{63}$)

7) £2.45 (3.5 x 0.7 = 2.45)

8) Eggs are $\frac{1}{21}$ of the total. ($\frac{6}{21}+\frac{14}{21}=\frac{20}{21}$)

9) No, it is $\frac{2}{15}$

10) 100 (She needs to improve by 80 x $\frac{1}{4}$ = 20; 80 + 20 = 100)

11) $2\frac{3}{8}$ ($\frac{7}{8}+\frac{12}{8}=\frac{19}{8}$)

12) 625 g ground beef (250 ÷ 2 x 5 = 625)

13) He has $\frac{1}{8}$ left. (24 – 12.50 – 8.50 = 3.00; $\frac{3}{24}=\frac{1}{8}$)

14) $\frac{1}{8}$

15) 27

16) $5\frac{5}{6}$ ($\frac{20}{6}+\frac{15}{6}=\frac{35}{6}$)

17) $4\frac{5}{8}$ ($\frac{63}{8}-\frac{26}{8}=\frac{37}{8}$)

18) £6.14 (9.21 x $\frac{1}{3}$ = 3.07; 9.21 – 3.07 = 6.14)

19) $5\frac{1}{3}$ (4 x $\frac{4}{3}=\frac{16}{3}$)

20) 16 total pens. (4x2) + (1x2) + (3x2) = 16

21) $20\frac{5}{8}$

22) Less ($20\frac{2}{7}$ < 21)

23) 42 (7 x 6 = 42 other chocolates)

24) £9.00 (10.80 ÷ 1.20 = 9.00)

25) 12 mints (He eats 90 x $\frac{1}{3}$ = 30, so 60 remain. 60 ÷ 5 = 12)

Answer Key

Time, pages 139 – 140

1) 336 (24 x 14 = 336)

2) 13 days

3) 7 (January, March, May, July, August, October, December)

4) 30 seconds

5) 13 hours, 33 minutes

6) Leap years will be 2024, 2028, 2032, 2036, etc.

7) 04:00 in New York

8) 86,400 seconds (60 sec x 60 min x 24 hours = 86,400)

9) 60 months (12 months x 5 years = 60)

10) 3,653 days (10 x 365 = 3650 + 3 = 3653)

11) Friday

12) 30 degrees

13) Driving with the friend would be faster (6:45pm vs 7:03pm arrival)

14) Less (3 x 60 + 14 = 194 minutes)

15) 8:37pm

16) 1,096 days (365 x 3 + 1 = 1,096)

17) The train is faster. It takes 4 hours, and the lorry takes 5 hours.

18) He can make 15 in one hour. (60 ÷ 4 = 15)

19) 4,800 seconds (25 x 3 + 5 = 80 minutes, 80 x 60 = 4,800)

20) 225 minutes (15 ÷ 4 = 3.75 hours, 3.75 x 60 = 225)

21) 153

22) 420 press-ups (30 x 14 = 420)

23) 20 minutes (1000ml = 1l, rate is 2 min per 100ml, so 2 x 10 = 20 min)

24) 7:35am

25) 745 hours (Sep = 30 x 24 = 720, 720 + 25 = 745)

Data & Graphs, Page 141 – 144

1) 13 (50 x .26 = 13)

2) 5 (Somerset had 15, Devon had 10)

3) 16 games

4) 48 goals

5) 3 goals per game (48 ÷ 16 = 3)

6) Between 12:00 and 13:00

7) 15:00

8) The 0830 train from Stoke is the fastest (47 minutes)

9) 22 minutes (0650 train takes 2hrs 2min, 0620 train takes 1hr 40min)

10) 0730

11) 25 minutes

12) 150 °C

13) After 15 minutes

14) 36 (72 – 36 = 36)

15) $^1/_{12}$ (Remember a circle has 360°, so $^{30}/_{360} = {}^1/_{12}$)

16) 15 (vanilla 36, mint 3, chocolate 12, Neapolitan 6, total 69; 72 – 69 = 15)

17) Haley

18) 2 – Ariel and Hailey

19) 135,000 bottles

20) 45,000 bottles (135,000 ÷ 3 = 45,000)

21) 21

22) Dog

23) Five (Aria, Trevor, Sophia, Simon, Willow)

24) $\frac{2}{5}$ (10 dog owners, of whom 4 own another pet)

25) 50% (6 total other pet owners, 3 have either a dog or cat or both)

Also available from the Armadillo's Pillow

The Big 11+ Vocabulary Play Book

- Learn over 1,000 words targeted specifically for Eleven Plus Exam
- 52 successfully tested, engaging activities – includes games, puzzles, cartoons, quizzes, rhymes and tongue twisters that address synonym, antonym, analogy, cloze and category questions in a lively way.
- All the materials are photocopiable
- Includes a full glossary of words and definitions

The Big 11+ Logic Puzzle Challenge

- A unique collection of logic puzzles to challenge and prepare children for the Eleven Plus as well as Independent School exams.
- Includes: Non-verbal reasoning, verbal reasoning, riddles and brain teasers, worded problems, spatial reasoning, cube nets, mazes and much more!
- The variety of challenges should stimulate and keep children interested as they improve their ability to solve different types of problems.

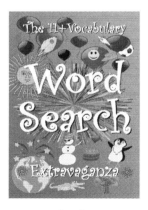

The 11+ Vocabulary Word Search

- Word Search book focused exclusively on vocabulary required for Eleven Plus exams
- Organised by synonyms, antonyms, subjects and themes
- Increase vocabulary retention and spelling through challenging word search puzzles
- Great companion book to *The Big 11+ Vocabulary Play Book*

 Contact us at: thearmadillospillow@gmail.com

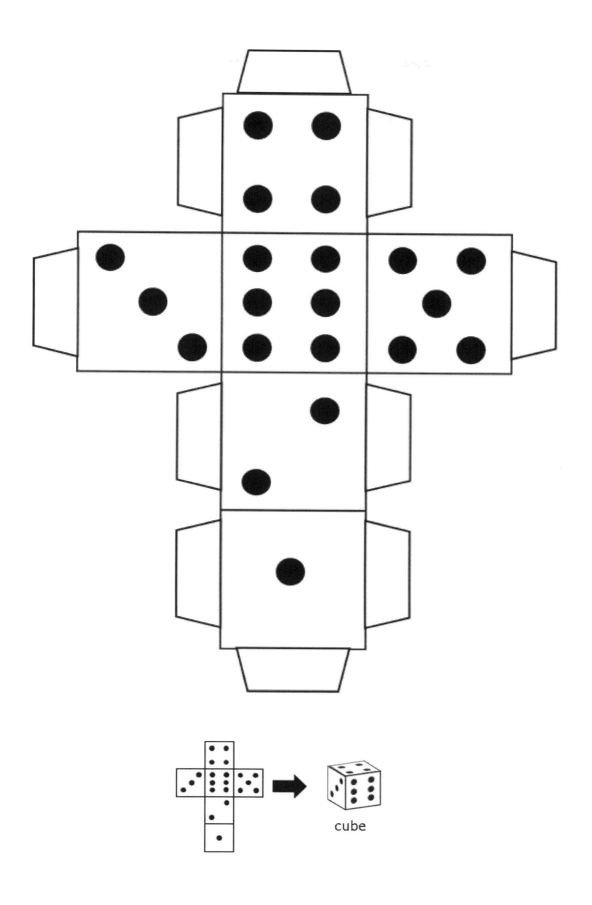

cube

Printed in Great Britain
by Amazon